Edinburgh Review 121

Made in Poland

Edinburgh Review

Published by Edinburgh Review
22a Buccleuch Place, Edinburgh EH8 9LN

edinburgh.review@ed.ac.uk
www.edinburghreview.org.uk

ISSN 0267 6672
Edinburgh Review 121 ISBN 978-0-9555745-1-1

Printed and bound in the UK
by The Cromwell Press Ltd, Trowbridge, Wiltshire

Individual subscriptions (3 issues annually) £17 / $27 / €27
Institutional subscriptions (3 issues annually) £34 / $54 / €54
You can subscribe online at www.edinburghreview.org.uk
or send a cheque to *Edinburgh Review*
22a Buccleuch Place, Edinburgh, EH8 9LN

Edinburgh Review
is supported by

Edinburgh Review is a partner magazine with eurozine www.eurozine.com

Contents

ARTICLES

PHOTOGRAPHS

Editorial

I ended my last editorial by saying, 'Next, we go to Poland...'; in fact, it has been more a case of Poland coming to us. Once a few initial enquiries had been made to writers and translators in Poland, word quickly spread that a Polish issue of *Edinburgh Review* was afoot, and we were sent far more work of a very high quality than we could possibly include, even though we increased the extent of the issue in an attempt to represent the range and depth of the material received.

Edinburgh Review combines a commitment to Scottish writing with an international perspective: each issue showcases the work of writers from another country, while exploring that country's historical and literary connections with Scotland. Here, we are proud to present fiction and poetry by major Polish writers such as Paweł Huelle, Tadeusz Różewicz and Wisława Szymborska, alongside work by writers who deserve to be better known in Britain. We hope that the articles on Polish culture and history will help to heighten our awareness and understanding of these things – a matter of some importance, now that Poland has indeed come to us.

The historical and literary connections are legion. Hannah Adcock documents an extraordinary experiment based on co-operation and mutual solidarity – the Polish School of Medicine, founded in Edinburgh in the dark days of 1941. In 'the Bread and Meat of Life', Will Brady examines the effects of the dismantling of communism on Poland's identity and culture, and considers the implications of the new wave of Polish immigration to the UK, finding cause for hope in the vibrant Polish community now thriving in Edinburgh – a community aptly celebrated in Desirée Elfström's photographs of Polish shops in the city. Catherine Czerkawska reflects movingly on her Polish heritage, as does the narrator of Merryn Glover's short story 'Broken Bread'. Even Scottish poet Ian McDonough's sequence, resolutely set in some of Scotland's less glamorous locations – 'Supermarket Car Park, Dalkeith' – by rolling together observation of the everyday and philosophical reflection, manages to have a strangely 'Polish' feel. At least, it does for this reader – but that may be because I have been thinking constantly about things Polish for as long as it has taken to bring 'Made in Poland' together, and because, as we hope this issue demonstrates, 'made in Poland' can sometimes also mean 'made in Scotland'.

Brian McCabe, Editor

Michał Lachman

Grapefruit Smiling
or Polish Theatre is Juicy

GEOLOGY—There have been few seismic changes in the Polish culture that require more imagination and creative thinking to be fully understood than the artistic revolution which swept across the stages after 1989. The shift from one theatrical epoch to another was only part of a larger tectonic movement which resulted in altering virtually every aspect of life, from the style of bus tickets to the rhetoric of the first democratically elected politicians. As all upheavals which are long-awaited and dreamt-about, ripening in people's minds before they materialise in action, the theatrical revolution of 1989 came as a complete surprise. The new theatre and drama fomenting in front of the baffled audience was everything but what they had expected. It was the most immediate, direct and vivid reflection of the new state and society emerging from under the shadow of political dictatorship, and as such it recorded the country's chaos, fear and exultation *in statu nascendi*. Now, almost two decades later, one can try to form more balanced opinions, weigh pros and cons, be objective. And – be happy.

LEAR'S FOOLS—Paradoxically, under the communist regime Polish theatre played almost non-theatrical roles. It was a substitute and a compensation for the lack of democratic parliament, free speech, and independent press. Yet, it was far from the verbatim immediacy of the Living Newspaper in the early twentieth century, or the famous documentary drama of today's stars – David Hare or Richard Norton-Taylor. Polish theatre was the nation's House of Commons and Hyde Park Corner in the realm of spirit and patriotic pride. It was defiantly frequented by those who believed in the undying resilience of national spirit and identity, in the continuity of Polish culture, in the community of internal émigrés who cultivated their secret and private rebellion. What is more, theatre provided moral guidance, reacted to political crises and responded to historical inevitabilities of the centrally planned economy by providing space for elusive and metaphorical dialogue with the regime. Actors and directors – masters of coded speech – posed as leaders, unable to lead the crowds into the streets but effectively riveting them in their plush chairs.

It does not come as a surprise that the repertoire was mostly based on revivals of the classics, Shakespeare and the Polish Romantics. That was where directors like Konrad Swinarski, Kazimierz Dejmek, Adam Hanuszkiewicz, Jerzy Jarocki, Andrzej Wajda and Jerzy Grzegorzewski found powerful metaphors and complex images to negotiate the terms on which the public debate was held. King Lear's question 'Dost thou call me a fool, boy?', which the regime remained unable to produce, was however indirectly suggested by stressing the Fool's answer: 'All thy other titles thou hast given away'. Kazimierz Dejmek's production of *Ghosts* in 1967, a Polish Romantic masterpiece of 1824 by Adam Mickiewicz, not only revived the memory of the Polish resistance to Russian occupation in the nineteenth century but also underlined the rebellious spirit of the Polish patriots sent to Siberia. The slightly reshaped text of the play as well as the audience's standing ovation at its premiere in the National Theatre in Warsaw were a powerful expression of independence and anger, which infuriated the Russian ambassador and above all other communist leaders. The crowds spilled into the streets and the Party was more than happy to suspend the production and use it as an excuse to justify its war against the 'class enemy'; finally, to orchestrate one of the most tragic anti-Semitic purges in Polish history.

FROM PUBLIC TO PRIVATE—The period immediately following the change of the system in 1989 was a time of reorientation and chaotic search for new forms and themes. With new names such as Krystian Lupa, Grzegorz

Jarzyna, Krzysztof Warlikowski and Anna Augustynowicz trickling slowly into public attention, a rough map of the new theatrical territory slowly began to take shape. The theatre of the first wave of new artists, also known as 'wise youngsters', was drastically anti-political. Instead of discussing politics, morality or the patriotic duties of art, these productions concentrated on the problems of style, on the aesthetics of the theatrical event, on the individual and his/her complex psychology. Polish theatre moved from its period of politicisation into a period of intense aesthetic stylisation and experiment. With that came the rejection of the known canons and traditions. Out went the Polish Romantics together with the literature of the national revival and spiritual sophistication. The father of the new theatrical generation, Krystian Lupa, honed his artistic idiom through staging work by Robert Musil (*The Dreamers*, *The Man Without Qualities*), Rainer Maria Rilke (*Malte*), Thomas Bernhard (*Kalkwerk*, *Immanuel Kant*, *Auslöschung*), Hermann Broch (*The Sleepwalkers*), Fyodor Dostoevsky (*The Brothers Karamazov*), Mikhail Bulgakov (*The Master and Margarita*) and Friedrich Nietzsche (*Thus Spake Zarathustra*).

Closely collaborating with the Stary Theatre and teaching at the Theatre Academy in Kraków, where he educated the first generation of the new directors, Lupa freed Polish stage from the obligation to debate national history. German decadent fiction, skilfully translated onto the stage, showed the path to explorations of the complexities of the individual mind, shifting focus from the public to the private. Such productions as *The Sleepwalkers*, *Brothers Karamazov* and *Auslöschung* succeeded in reconnecting Polish theatre with contemporary culture and encouraged discussion about the state of today's Europe, presenting the condition of modern man as a representation of European cultural heritage. Lupa's *Kalkwerk* (*The Lime Works*, 1992), based on Thomas Bernhard's novel, was a five-hour study of the internal labyrinth of a mind desperately trying to fight its own incompletion, inconsistency and alienation from the outside world. The closed and inexplicable universe of sounds, smells and other sensory perceptions of a hypersensitive intellectual, who – ironically – works on a treatise on hearing, was represented by the steel and concrete construction of the lime works building. The closing image of the play showed his wife obsessively powdering her face in a ballet-like rhythm. Wielding a bushy brush, veiled in a haze of white powder, she was slowly covering herself with the multilayered defensive shield which indicated the utter desperation of individuals disconnected and alienated from each other and from the world outside.

Lupa's *Auslöschung* (2001) was concerned with the ethical aspects of erasing the memory of the Nazi past in Austria. It unintentionally coincided with the debate about Jedwabne – a small town in north-eastern Poland and the place of a ruthless pogrom perpetrated by Polish citizens on their Jewish neighbours. Through the story of Franz Murau's attempts to clean up his family's past, the play provided a relevant commentary about the polemical divisions in Polish society and media. What is more, Lupa's work sent a clear message – that theatre matters, even if it does not choose to talk about hermetically Polish and stereotypically national 'obsessions'. He proved that universal moral problems could make a relevant state-of-the-nation play.

VISCERAL CLEANSING—The new theatre directors who had their debuts after 1989 – Krzysztof Warlikowski, Grzegorz Jarzyna, Anna Augustynowicz – were the last group who tasted the real communist regime of the 1980s, when they were in their teens. In this generation, the police state of Martial Law, the Gdańsk shipyard and Solidarity were for them what Margaret Thatcher and the coal miners' strike represented for British playwrights like Mark Ravenhill and artists like Damian Hirst. They were brought up in the same grey landscape of dilapidated high-rise buildings, dirty streets, poverty and fear – only much worse, with food rationing, night curfew, undercover agents, Russian tanks on the border and pre-emptive murders of the secret police. These directors all seem to have rejected the heroics of the 'democratic opposition' of Lech Wałęsa. Krzysztof Warlikowski, an unwilling leader of the whole group, once said of Solidarity: 'It wasn't my cup of tea. When my high school friends were sent to jail for smuggling illegal publications, I was completely disinterested. I lived in a private world of books and intellectual discussions.' Their attitude towards the Polish theatrical and historical tradition was, then, not that of conflict and rebellion but of indifference.

The two names which stormed the theatrical Bastille in Poland were Krzysztof Warlikowski and Grzegorz Jarzyna, who were associated with the Rozmaitości Theatre in Warsaw. In the second half of the 1990s, they created a theatrical institution which found its own audience and developed its own aesthetics of hip, postmodern, urban theatre. What was perhaps even more important for their young metropolitan audiences was that the Rozmaitości, with Jarzyna as the artistic manager and Warlikowski as its director, grew to represent a completely new style of acting and performance. Programmatically destroying the realistic fourth-wall illusion, sometimes almost non-representational, ironic and distanced, it explored raw, visceral emotions through techniques ranging from Brechtian alienation to physical theatre. As the hottest venue in town, the Rozmaitości bridged the gap between the stage and the audience by inventing a program called TR Warszawa (Out In Town Project) which comprised not only creative writing classes and acting or directing workshops for young apprentice artists but also a number of performances staged outside the theatre building, in most unexpected locations: the central railway station, private apartments, abandoned squats. The Rozmaitości penetrated other areas of public activity by opening up for guest lectures, public debates and artistic happenings. It turned into an institution which engaged the community at large.

Two most memorable and epoch-defining productions were Sarah Kane's *Cleansed* (dir. Warlikowski, a co-production with the Współczesny Theatre in Wrocław and the Współczesny Theatre in Poznań, 2001) and *4.48 Psychosis* (dir. Jarzyna, 2002). In order to visualise the splash which Kane's writing had in the Polish theatre, the impact she had on the British stage and reviewers needs to be doubled or tripled. The distance which Polish audiences had to cover from the metaphorical productions of the classics or the nineteenth-century literature to Kane's imagery was unfathomably larger than that between *Blasted* or *Cleansed* and, say, Caryl Churchill's *Cloud Nine* or Howard Brenton's *Romans in Britain*. *Cleansed* and *4.48 Psychosis* injected new themes and completely new imagery into theatrical circulation. Warlikowski's rendering of onstage violence in *Cleansed* was indirect, poetic, almost discreet, shifting attention to those aspects of human psyche which produce it, rather than exposing the muscles which do the cutting – dismembering the characters' bodies is used by Kane to represent personal and institutional oppression and violence. Interlaced with oneiric and bucolic film projections *Cleansed* was a slowly paced meditation on vulnerability, using nudity and intimacy as contexts for the philosophical dialogues. In Warlikowski's production, Kane's characters were primarily emotional, hypersensitive, even hysterical individuals whose otherness was put into high relief by testing the limits of their bodies' durability. In contrast, *4.48 Psychosis* is an explosion of energy and anger, through the voice of a patient kept in a mental asylum and exposed to severe medicalisation.

Under Jarzyna's guidance, her suffering, rebellion and frustration evolved into a fascinating piece of physical theatre in which the human body is literally assaulted by the outside world. The scenes in which the actress's naked body is pierced through by millions of projected digits representing doses of medicines, or the closing scene in which the actress smashes herself against the wall, remain the most powerful manifestations of the sensibilities of the new Polish theatre. The play's uncompromising sincerity, extreme exhibitionism, physicality, anti-illusionist dialogue and setting became the freshly coined dialect with which the conversation with the modern world could be maintained. Yet, some critics felt offended and morally blackmailed either to love it or be damned. Of course, to the Rozmaitości's devoted following this was the predictable reaction of middle-aged men stranded in a house full of applauding teenagers.

THEY COME TO BURN DOWN YOUR HOUSE—Without any doubt these two productions opened the floodgates for new theatre, new criticism and new writing. The Rozmaitości crew had to bear the brunt of criticism from conservative reviewers. The war of words was waged not only on the pages of professional theatre journals but out in the open, between critics, journalists, musicians and writers. Directors at the Rozmaitości and a handful of of others elsewhere created centres of intense activity pioneering different and fascinating ways of making theatre in and for contemporary Poland. This plurality of voices, which included Paweł Miśkiewicz, Piotr Cieplak, Anna Augustynowicz, Paweł Szkotak, Zbigniew Brzoza, Mariusz Grzegorzek, changed the face of theatre and gradually got right into its entrails. A host of adventurous productions – Anton Chekhov's *Cherry Orchard* (dir. Paweł Miśkiewicz, 2001) Clare McIntyre's *Low Level Panic* (dir. Anna Augustynowicz, 1995), Peter Handke's *The Hour When We Knew Nothing about Each Other* (dir. Zbigniew Brzoza, 1996) and many others sent Polish theatre spinning into the new millennium. What is more, theatre festivals – Dialog in Wrocław, Kontakt in Toruń, buz@rt in Kraków and Malta in Poznań – gave Polish audiences an exceptional opportunity to watch the best and most famous productions from Lithuania, Estonia, Russia, Germany, France and Britain. Exchange of ideas and inspiration was the natural consequence of these encounters with the work of René Pollesch, Christoph Marthaler, Luk Perceval, Maguy Marin, Complicite Theatre Company and many more. Yet, perhaps the most significant aspect of the new theatrical revival is the fact that it reaches communities off-centre, outside Warsaw, in towns like Legnica, Radom, Otwock, Gdynia, Wrocław, Poznań or Łódź, where local theatre people learn the difficult skill of talking to their own audiences about their own problems.

The generation of the 'wise youngsters' reconnected with European drama, brought foreign names like Sarah Kane, Mark Ravenhill, Marius von Mayenburg, Werner Schwab and Bernard-Marie Koltes to Polish stages, and produced highly intellectual, aesthetically lush and largely urban theatre intended for the privileged audiences of the metropolitan elite; it was the next group of directors, born in the 1970s, educated into the rampant capitalism of the young Polish democracy and given the label of the 'new disappointed', that carried theatre to the provinces. (Both of these labels and their definitions were brilliantly coined by Piotr Gruszczyński, one of the most important commentators of the new drama and theatre in Poland.) They concentrated on the victims of the newborn consumer culture, those who got stuck in the gears of violent capitalism and futile social reform. People like Jan Klata, Maja Kleczewska, Michał Zadara, Łukasz Barczyk, Piotr Rubin, Przemysław Wojcieszek, Paweł Demirski tend to make 'community theatre', working with the stories of local people. They are interested in authentic texts, the documentary rendering of facts, with straightforward communication. What is more, they are angry: they persist in asking awkward questions and often give unfair answers; they are destroyers who seem to believe in the strategy of the burnt ground. Two poignant images exemplify the difference between the two generations and their aesthetic priorities. In the Rozmaitości's Bacchae, directed by Warlikowski in 2001, the queer and seductive Dionysus leads his female followers to frenzy which ends with Pentheus' head stuck on a long pole and two steel buckets full of bloody offal representing his destroyed body. This image of grotesque mannerism and disgusting violence, suspended somewhere between metaphysics and butchery, stands in shocking contrast to what we find in *Made in Poland* (2004), a production from the Helena Modrzejewska Theatre in Legnica, a small town in southern Poland. The play, written and directed by Przemysław Wojcieszek, tells the story of Bogus, a teenager from an underdeveloped district in Legnica. A former altar boy, he becomes disappointed with his spiritual leaders, the priest and the school teacher, and goes on the rampage through the neighbourhood with a metal pipe in his hand and the warning 'Fuck off' tattooed on his forehead. The production's iconic image occurs at the very beginning: Bogus smashes a car in front of the theatre before the action moves into an abandoned supermarket where the audience take their seats. His anger and violent temper are rooted in social and economic issues; from his discussions with a priest and a teacher, all three emerge as victims of the 'Polish miracle', which went askew.

The Helena Modrzejewska Theatre's mission statement declares that the actors want to meet their audiences 'in the theatre whose stage is the city'. Committed to a very clear anti-establishment philosophy, they penetrate the forgotten, 'negative spaces' of communities, far away from the glitzy ostentation of Warsaw's posh theatres. They make theatre based on 'real stories in real places'. Apart form *Made in Poland*, their most famous production is *The Ballad of Zakaczawie* (2001) – Zakaczawie being a district notorious for crime and violence. The production consisted of stories built on interviews with the local residents, thieves, priests and the police. Authentic objects from private owners were used as props, and the atmosphere of communist times was recreated through characters based on real people.

A similar interest in the personal and private combined with a strong social and subversive message is characteristic of the Theatre Wybrzeże in Gdańsk and especially their experimental form called 'quick urban theatre'. Invented by Paweł Demirski after his workshop at London's Royal Court, 'quick urban theatre' was a semi-documentary form of presenting real-life stories in non-theatrical venues. This environmental theatre of rebellious social intervention tackled contentious issues of the contemporary Polish society. *Ours* was a report on Polish Neo-Nazi, *Down* presented a series of interviews with the families of Polish soldiers in Iraq, and *Don't Be Surprised When They Come to Burn Down Your House* investigated the tragic death of a man accidentally killed in a factory producing household appliances.

Like the first group of artists with Warlikowski and Jarzyna at its head, who were criticised for immorality and disrespect for the tradition of sacred art, the second generation of artists is represented by its detractors as vulgar, iconoclastic, superficial and journalistic. Yet, without sustained probing into taboo topics, the fundamental role of theatre as a public art would not be fulfilled. As Artaud once said, the role of theatre is to 'drain abscesses'. These young artists may be seen as a necessary virus, the plague which purifies.

MADE IN POLAND—The new Polish drama followed the first generation of the directors and arrived, so to speak, when the demand for contemporary Polish writing for theatre had already been conspicuously growing. In the mid-1990s, the first signs of change could be seen. Following Grzegorz Nawrocki's *Young Death* (1995), a play about juvenile murderers, there arrived a string of texts written mainly by people who had come to theatre from other fields and occupations. Script writers and film directors Paweł Sala and Przemysław Wojcieszek, the architect Krzysztof Bizio and the medical doctor Marek Modzelewski investigated problems faced by individuals in a society on the fast track to material prosperity. Even when this work was formally deficient, it communicated an extremely powerful message. Lashing against most sacred pieties, those playwrights skinned 1990s' Poland with their bare hands, exposing its veins and tendons. They did not bother to mince their words or censor the content. No territory, however taboo, was off limits.

Jan Klata's *Grapefruit Smiling* (2003), with characters named %, &, <, @ and $, tells a story of journalists in the Vatican awaiting the Pope's death. Terminally bored, they mange to miss the moment, while watching David Beckham's TV coverage. *Toxins* (2002) by Krzysztof Bizio is a series of short sketches presenting violent alcoholics and drug pushers attempting to play the roles of fathers and educators to the younger generation. Marek Modzelewski's *Coronation* (2003) is a bleak tale of a medical doctor in his thirties who realises the utter futility of his life and marriage. Paweł Demirski's documentary *From Poland With Love* (2004) was invented during creative writing workshops at the Royal Court in London and showed the nasty and disappointing underbelly of the supposedly successful emigration of young Poles to England, while Anna Burzyńska's *Most Suicides Happen on Sunday* (2004) attempts to reconstruct the mentality of modern teenagers lost between the search for identity and the search for pleasure.

Most of these young voices are extremely emotional, to some, hysterical; they are aggressive and – characteristically – they desperately hark for 'the enemy'; when one does not exist, it must be invented. Their work has been anthologised in a two-volume publication edited by Roman Pawłowski, a theatre critic from *Gazeta Wyborcza* – one of the biggest and most influential dailies in Poland. The titles of the volumes, *Porno Generation* and *Made in Poland*, had the impact similar to *In-Yer-Face Theatre*, Aleks Sierz's book on the British drama in the 1990s. The 'porno generation' emerged as the brand name for this controversial group of playwrights. Their plays are sometimes accused of being little more than a string of verbatim quotes, a mirror-image of the everyday world, with negligible artistic merit. However, they remain a sound sociological diagnosis of the generational discontent. 'Generation Nothing' (so named after Kuba Wandachowicz's 'manifesto' was published in *Gazeta Wyborcza*), refers to a group of people born in the late 1970s or early 1980s, the proverbial 'people without qualities' or, to use the vernacular, a 'generation without adjectives'. The Polish 'Nothing-land' (the title of a play by Anna Burzyńska) paradoxically offers something, if it is to be judged by the chord it strikes with, mainly young, audiences and some critics. Even if it is 'merely' a journalistic record of life outside the window, or as George Steiner would call it 'the false authenticity of the immediate', the movement is showing signs of increasing versatility and innovation, with such divergent trends as the Komuna Otwock, an anarchic experimental theatre group interested in issues from the sociology of the Holocaust (*Perehodnik/Bauman*) to the possibility of revolution in the style of Baader-Meinhof (*The Future of the World*), and the feminist drama of Lidia Amejko and Maria Wojtyszko.

Polish theatre has a very long way to go, new areas to conquer – women's drama, minority drama, gay and lesbian drama and serious political drama still remain territories largely unexplored. However, judging by the amount of steam under the lid, we have a great feast ahead.

Further Reference

Gruszczyński, Piotr, *Ojcobójcy. Młodsi zdolniejsi w teatrze polskim*, Wydawnictwo W.A.B., Warszawa, 2003

Kopciński, Jacek, *Którędy do wyjścia. Szkice i rozmowy teatralne*, Oficyna Wydawnicza Errata, Wydawnictwo Uniwersytetu Kardynała Stefana Wyszyńskiego, Warszawa, 2002.

Pawłowski, Roman ed. *Pokolenie Porno i inne niesmaczne utwory teatralne*, Wydawnictwo Zielona Sowa, Kraków 2003.

Pawłowski, Roman ed. *Made in Poland. Dziewięć sztuk teatralnych z polski w wyborze Romana Pawłowskiego*, Korporacja HA!A & Horyzont, Kraków, 2006.

Plata, Tomasz ed., *Strategie publiczne, strategie prywatne. Teatr polski 1990–2005*, Świat Literacki, Izabelin, 2006.

http://www.culture.pl/en/culture/

Two poems by Jacek Dehnel

translated by Antonia Lloyd-Jones

Symmetry

for P.T.

We lie further and further apart. It's the same old
bed, the same old sheets, but we're apart, further and further.
Like a bat-pollinated flower, the bed opens,
spreading wide each evening – with us on opposing
petals. Further and further away. We lie parted.
We cannot reach out a hand, never make foot contact –
from your shore come the sound of orioles and the growling
of wildcats, on mine grebes are seen and, very rarely,
an ermine, that has darted into the dense bedding.
Wider and wider. Castles of stone and sluices,
full harbours, gardens, boundless wilderness and deserts.

Each on his own still side of the night. Parallel in
our solitude and silence. There's no way to summon,
there's no way to stand over the abyss and listen.
Untied, unknotted bindings, rhymes loose, unencumbered.
Nearer the door and windows than each other. We slumber.

Łódź-Warsaw, 8 December 2003

FOTO-FILM, A. Cechnowski, Łódź, Passage 24, tel. 457–23

There's still a Jew with a woolly beard, under a kalpak
artfully tied with ribbon, someone's playing a donkey
in a fur coat – the remnant of a Sunday-best from Riga,
there's a Priest, live and kicking, although he is standing
against the blackboard; the Magi, as through all the centuries
of primary school plays: a gilded piece of cardboard and sceptres
made of lathe-turned chair legs. Next to the Boy Shepherds
in their embroidered jerkins, one with his hat tilted
down at a rakish angle over his nine-year-old
eye. There's a mountain of whiteness, golden thread and plumage:
little round faces in a general fluff of angel purity,
headbands emitting sunbeams from shining, precisely
brushed and combed tresses – the higher up the picture,
the more Stars, with their pointed heads close to the ceiling
(a bit part in the Nativity Play – even the comet –
is something that can mark you for the rest of your life).

Only the girl in the headdress, with the plastic baby,
gazes further and deeper, more intensely, strangely
over the hooded camera, over the children's tutor;
it's nineteen-thirty-seven. The line-up is lacking
the Devil and Death. They're crossing the frozen lakes.

Warsaw, 2 November 2005

Hannah Adcock

The Polish School of Medicine, Edinburgh

In the dark days of 1941, when Hitler controlled most of Europe and millions of people were fighting for their lives, an extraordinary experiment based on mutual co-operation and solidarity was attempted in Scotland's capital city. This was the founding of the Polish School of Medicine, attached to the University of Edinburgh and the brainchild of Brigadier Professor Crew, a member of the Faculty of Medicine and Commanding Officer of the Military Hospital at Edinburgh Castle. The school would be a Polish faculty, providing Polish staff where possible and steering students towards a Polish medical diploma, but its students would matriculate at the University and have all the rights of a Scottish student.

The Polish forces based in Scotland at the time contained a substantial number whose medical studies had been disrupted, whilst the Medical Corps of the Polish army contained a significant number of professors and lecturers. The students were keen to finish their training and depart for the front line; the lecturers were equally determined to support the war effort by training them. Also, and importantly, the Medical School would enable Poles to continue their admired academic and cultural tradition at a time when Hitler was determined to turn their country into 'an intellectual desert'. The final agreement was signed on 24 February 1941, between the

Polish government in exile in London, and the University of Edinburgh. The President of Poland, Mr W. Raczkiewicz, formally proclaimed the opening of the Polish School of Medicine on 22 March in the presence of university authorities. The Vice Chancellor and Principal of the University, Sir Thomas Holland, opened the ceremony with the following words:

> We have met today for a ceremony which is unique in the history of this University, and, so far as I know, without precedent of any sort; for the circumstances in which the Government of Poland and the authorities of this University have agreed on a measure of union have never, since universities were founded, occurred in the civilised world.

However, cultural associations between Scotland and Poland already stretched back over the centuries, so although the Medical School venture was unique, the spirit of mutual respect and co-operation was well established. Adventurous Scots had been arriving in Poland since at least the fifteenth century. They were a mixed bunch, some looking for a quick diversion, others hoping to stay and make a life away from religious strife and poor prospects. Not all of them stayed in towns and cities. The phrase 'a Scots peddlar's pack in Poland' became almost proverbial in seventeenth-century England and probably contained at least a modicum of truth. Higher up the social ladder, a privileged group of Scottish merchants supplied provisions to the Polish army and Royal Court. Poles at that time did not appear quite as enamoured with trade as their northern counterparts, and wily Scots were keen to exploit this divergence in economic ambition. At the very highest rung of society, connection between the two countries was cemented by marriage. Count Andrew Morsztyn, statesman and poet, married Lady Catherine Gordon, daughter of the second Marquis of Huntly, in 1659.

The years from 1466 to 1648 were halcyon days for Poland as she largely held onto an ideal of religious tolerance and strong statehood, whilst the rest of Europe was ripped open by religious schism. She was an attractive migration destination – a land of Eastern opportunity. However, this was to change after the mid-seventeenth century as foreign invasions and government inefficiency caused a steady deterioration in her power.

Most Scottish merchants and immigrants did not forget their homeland – or their religion – and it was through a number of bequests that links between Polish students and the University of Edinburgh were first initiated. Daniel Davisson was born in Poland, the son of a Scot, and settled in Danzig. Like many of his countrymen, he tried to help the Reformed Church and to this end endowed in 1688 a stipend for one or two scholars to go abroad and study divinity. Later, the document was amended to specify that students, either of Scottish or Polish descent, must go to either Leyden or Edinburgh. Similarly, Robert Brown, born in Scotland but a merchant of Zamosc, stipulated in his will that a fund was to be set up in his name to allow one Scottish and one Polish scholar, both of the Protestant persuasion, to study at Edinburgh University. 'After so long a peregrination in this Kingdom of Poland' he appreciated the value of his adoptive country whilst retaining a love for the country of his birth. Owing most probably to his bursary, several students arrived in Edinburgh from Poland in the eighteenth century to study divinity and the arts. Although they have their nationality as *Polonus*, many bore typical Scottish names like Inglis and Aram. These bursary students were the privileged few, unusual in any case for their affiliation to the Protestant cause.

From the end of the eighteenth century, a new wave of Polish students arrived in Edinburgh, of noble lineage and Catholic faith. Rather than studying divinity, they opted for the arts or medicine. Andrew Sniadecki took medical courses taught by A. Duncan, Alexander Munro and James Gregory before returning to Poland to organise the study of medicine at the University of Vilna, using his foreign experience. He is the author of *The Theory of Organic Substances*, which was translated into German and French. Another student was Dr Adam Lyszczynski, a post-1830–31 uprising émigré, who studied at the Medical School in Edinburgh and pursued a career in homeopathic medicine. Lyszczynski, his Scottish wife and their family settled in Edinburgh, in Warriston Crescent. Lyszczynski met Chopin on the train to Edinburgh and invited the composer to stay at his house during his Scottish visit of 1848. The piano Chopin played is still in the house and was played regularly by members of the Polish Chopin Circle, which met there for many years. Then of course there was that most famous Pole, Maria Skłodowska-Curie, who was awarded the Honorary Degree of Doctor of Laws by Edinburgh University in 1909.

For many centuries then, Scotland and Poland have been involved in the exchange of citizens and skills. During Poland's Golden Age the impulse was more for Scots to move abroad; in later centuries, the pendulum swung the other way, particularly as Edinburgh University's Medical School established a worldwide reputation. The 227 students to graduate from the Polish Medical School during and just after the Second World War were therefore following in the footsteps of their forefathers – and were welcomed as 'gallant allies'.

Initially the school provided education for medical students in the Polish forces evacuated after the fall of France, but they were later joined by compatriots from the Middle East and a small number of other students who completed their secondary school education in Great Britain. From the very beginning, the students, including women, formed friendly links with their Scottish counterparts. A number of articles written by Polish students appeared in Edinburgh University Student's periodical and in 1946–47 Gertruda Euklińska-Kolibabka was elected President of the Edinburgh University Student's Women Union.

The 'experiment' also soon proved to be a fine example of how finite resources could be shared to the benefit of all. The University provided all the laboratory and clinical facilities, whilst clinical instruction was given in Edinburgh hospitals and in the Polish Paderewski Hospital, established for Polish civilians and soldiers. There were ten Polish professors, about thirty senior and junior lecturers, and a handful of Scottish professors. Attached to them were Polish lecturers, but examinations were held in English. Students had to be extremely dedicated to study medicine and simultaneously learn a new language. Lt Colonel Dr Antoni Jurasz, Professor of Surgery at the University of Poznan, was the first Dean. The School was so successful that other faculties were founded: the Polish School of Architecture at the University of Liverpool, the Polish Veterinary Study at the Royal (Dick) Veterinary College in Edinburgh and the Polish Faculty of Law at the University of Oxford. All of them were established on the Edinburgh pattern.

Meanwhile, in Poland, clandestine medical schools were organised despite the watchful eye of the Germans. At first classes were held in secret, but subsequently in the open in technical schools and hospitals, deceiving the Germans into believing that they were designed to train medical assistants, rather than doctors. Some 4,000 medical and pharmacy students were educated, facilitating the opening of ten faculties of medicine as soon as the occupation ended. Edinburgh students returned to their units after graduation and took part in the invasion of Europe. The School stopped matriculating students in 1945 and finally closed in 1949.

After the war, some Polish doctors returned to Scotland, whilst others dispersed all over the globe. Their diplomas were recognised in Great Britain by an Act of Parliament in 1947. Some doctors enjoyed considerable success: Professor Rostowski, who had continued as Dean after the retirement of Professor Jurasz, was appointed as Consultant Neurologist to the Royal Edinburgh Hospital for Mental Disorders and held this post from 1949–54, when he reached the age of seventy. He was remembered with affection as being, in his youth, 'the best dancer among the neurologists and the best neurologist amongst the dancers' and was awarded a Honorary Degree of Doctor of Laws by Edinburgh University at the Jubilee Meeting of the Medical School in 1966.

Although large-scale displacements, *emigracja,* had become a defining characteristic of Polish life, permanent exile was not what most of the young doctors and their professors had anticipated. After years of bloodshed, away from family and roots, they wanted to return home to a free Poland. But the military and political direction of the war changed when Germany invaded the Soviet Union, the Soviets joined the Allies, and the USA and Britain placed Poland firmly in the Soviet Union's sphere of influence. Even before the war, communism held a keen attraction for the British Labour Party and certain members of the intelligentsia. In contrast, the Catholicism and anti-communism of the Poles started to prove unpopular in Britain, particularly because the media and government encouraged a pro-Soviet stance, fundamentally detrimental to the Poles. If there was any lingering doubt about their marginality, it was dispelled by the Tehran Conference (codenamed 'Eureka') in late 1943. Poles were conspicuously absent when Churchill and Roosevelt agreed, amongst other things, that Stalin would be allowed to annex Poland's eastern provinces at the end of the war.

It must have been difficult for the medical students – at once grateful to Edinburgh University for its generosity, whilst also feeling betrayed by the political manoeuvres of Britain and the USA. But if the British body politic was not as loyal to her Polish allies as might have been wished, the Polish medical students, at least, proved grateful recipients of Edinburgh's generosity. In the preface to the *Album of the Polish Medical School,* published in 1983, Lord Swan wrote, 'And in all its 400 years the University cannot, I think, have acquired a group of alumni more splendidly loyal to their Alma Mater.'

In 1949 graduates erected a bronze plaque in the quadrangle of the Medical Faculty, recalling to mind, 'the Magnanimous Gesture of the University at the time of the greatest misfortune for Poland'. The plaque was unveiled by Professor Rostowski and was his last act as Dean of the Medical School.

Although the Medical School physically ceased to exist in 1949, it has lived on in different forms. The Memorial Fund, which supports scholarships, the Professor Antoni Jurasz Lectureship and the Polish Historical Collection were all set up in 1986 on the 45th anniversary of the founding of the Medical School. Fundraising efforts were spearheaded by a small group of Canadian and American graduates (Drs Soból, Grzybowski and Wielhorski and Professors Kulczycki and Majeranowski) and continue to this day. It was and still is common for graduates or their families to donate money to the Fund in lieu of wedding gifts, funeral flowers etc. The largest donation to date, of half a million pounds, came from the estate of Oskar Słowik, a Canadian graduate. The Fund offers short scholarships to Polish medical doctors who wish to study at Edinburgh University and it also provides funding for a Head of Department from the Medical School in Edinburgh to lecture in Poland every three or four years. The first lecture is always at Poznan Medical University, the second at another university medical school in Poland. The lecture tour was instigated to further develop academic relationships between Scotland and Poland; the Historical Collection recalls the historic link between the two countries and celebrates the life of the Polish Medical School.

Dr Wiktor Tomaszewski, who was a senior staff member of the Polish Medical School from 1941 to 1949, remained in Edinburgh working as a general medical practitioner and went on to play a key part in keeping its memory alive. He took a leading role in organising the quinquennial Alumni gatherings in Edinburgh, gave generous support to the fund, the scholarship and lectureship programmes and established the Polish School of Medicine Historical Collection. He was awarded honorary doctorates by the University of Poznan in 1985 and by the University of Edinburgh in 1991 in recognition of his contribution to developing Scottish–Polish medical links. This year Dr Maria Długolecka-Graham and Mr Cecil Graham commissioned a Dr Wiktor Tomaszewski Centenary Medal. The commissioning of celebratory medals has a long and illustrious history in Poland.

The medal is on view in the collection in the Chancellor's Building, Little France, along with many other artefacts, including five powerful sculptures by Professor Rostowski. Dr Długolecka-Graham, herself half-Polish and a graduate of Edinburgh's Medical School, manages the collection, scholarships, reunions and future projects; in appreciation of her considerable efforts, she was presented with the Knight's Cross of the Order of Merit of the Republic of Poland earlier this year. She says, 'The Polish School of Medicine was a unique wartime venture and it has given us a truly wonderful legacy. I feel very privileged to be part of it. It allows me to express and celebrate my Polishness and to say thank you in a particularly meaningful way to my family and all the many people in these two wonderful countries, Scotland and Poland, who helped shape my life and me as a person. Indeed it encourages us all to celebrate and extend our rich Scottish–Polish heritage.'

The latest Polish Medical School linked initiative is the University of Edinburgh's £3.5 million fundraising project to establish a Polish School of Medicine Chair in Emergency Medicine, an endeavour seen as a particularly fitting because so many of the Polish graduates went back to use their medical skills on the front line during the war.

The Medical School and its legacy have always been about co-operation and mutual benefit. Many Polish doctors maintain and develop the links they made during their time in Edinburgh, supporting junior colleagues who are keen to apply for scholarships. Dr Długolecka-Graham maintains contact with past scholars and graduates of the Polish Medical School through newsletters, emails, cards and letters. On visits to Poland she organises gatherings, where past scholars can meet and reminisce and potential applicants can find out what the scholarship programme has to offer.

Dr Michael Szuber, a recent scholarship student, aptly describes Dr Długolecka-Graham as an 'ocean of initiative'. Her energies know no bounds: at the celebration to mark the opening of the Polish Room in the Chancellor's Building, she reproduced one of Professor Rostowski's sculptures in fondant icing for the top of the cake!

Two early poems by Tadeusz Różewicz

translated by Adam Czerniawski

A Rose

A rose is a flower
or the name of a dead girl

A rose may be placed in a warm hand
or in black earth

A red rose shouts
a golden-haired girl silently departs

Blood escaped from a pale petal
shape has abandoned a girl's dress

A gardener lovingly tends the plant
the rescued father loses his mind

It's five years since you died
a flower of love without thorns

Today a rose blossomed in the garden
faith and the memory of the living are dead
1945

The Moon Shines

the moon shines
an empty street
the moon shines
a man flees

the moon shines
a man falls
a man fades
the moon shines

the moon shines
an empty street
a dead man's face
a pool of water

Agata Masłowska

Twiddling

Pressing her feverish forehead against the glass pane, Lucy was searching for the right word to begin her book. Shouldn't it begin with an 'f'? She grabbed the pencil and scribbled down random words streaming into her, head: *first, face, fabulous, faff, from, false, fail.* 'Fuck!' she grunted angrily throwing the notebook on the floor. 'Bloody writing… I WILL write it, I will!' she exclaimed to her blurred reflection in the window. Her face looked distant and strange, distorted by the dark shapes outside. The reflection of her eyes overlapped with the square windows of the house opposite, the roof forming a spiky hat on the top of her head. Lucy was looking at her bizarre cubic image with amazement, as if she was seeing her face for the first time. 'That's it, that's it, my head as a house, that's it,' she murmured and began walking around the room. Every so often, she stopped, touched her face with the palm of her hand and went on walking. The house, the face, the windows, the eyes, the house in the head in the house, the head in the house in the head, one closed within another, like Russian babushkas. Her heart was pounding like mad and her face was drenched with sweat. The room seemed to be spinning as she kept on circling about it restlessly. The wall, the window, the wall, the door, the wall, the window… suddenly Lucy felt the floor escaping from her feet as her exhausted body folded down like a paper concertina on the thick soft carpet covered with balls of paper, pencils and dozens of creased tissues. It was one of her habits to jot down an idea or a sentence on tissues, which she folded and squeezed into her pocket. At the end of each week she would empty the pockets and look through the tissues, throwing some of them away and sticking the rest in her diary. Her ideas usually referred to God, the Universe, general sensations, or such trivial thoughts as the itching sole of her foot that she loved writing about the most. Lucy boasted in her mind that she was probably the only person in the world to write about the sole of a foot. It was now her intention to write a novel about it. 'Just imagine,' she was saying to herself, 'three or four hundred wonderful pages depicting the foot and the act of scratching it!' It is not that she wanted to become a writer. The very idea of becoming anybody or anything that could be labelled with this or that name filled her with sheer disgust. After all, she regarded all writers as phonies writing about stuff they had no idea about. Lucy was more than fed-up with all the worn-out images of love, loneliness, Weltschmerz, injustice or fear. Words have gone threadbare through overuse, she thought. Exhausted, she whispered, trying to catch her breath. An infinite number of fake pages, well, maybe apart from Proust, he wasn't too bad, Lucy thought, wiping sweat off her face with the back of her hand. The whirling ceiling was slowly coming to a standstill, her body filled with the sensation of arriving on the floor, so soft and silent. The bulb in the lamp flickered quickly a few times and its light became dimmer. She was lying on the floor breathing deeply, her eyes closed and mouth opened slightly letting drops of saliva fall on the carpet.

'French feet fiddle around…' Lucy noted the phrase down and continued looking at the map hanging on the wall of her room. China reminded her of the woman standing at the bus stop telling her friend about the book she had read. The book was about life, the woman exclaimed enthusiastically, life that goes in circles. Hope is out there, she said, quoting the book, because there is something waiting behind the wooden door. It is a comforting thought, the woman said. The book was about a Chinese guy called Tao or something. Lucy looked at her right foot, then her left foot, she slipped off her pink deck shoes, wiggled the toes, and moved her feet round to the inside and outside. Life goes in circles, how could this possibly be a comforting idea, Lucy wondered. She felt the spinning of her own life trapping her within.

She thought of her father and the day he decided to 'take matters in hand', of the phone ringing and someone saying slowly that there had been an accident and, after a long pause, 'your father is dead'. The body was covered with a white sheet, as white as Lucy's face when she noticed purple lines and bruises around his neck. Life goes in circles, maybe it does so better in China, maybe it expands into a multi-dimensional spiral allowing for unspeakable experiences everybody longs for. She felt that her life spiral was closing up around her and almost suffocating her, just like the spiral of her dad. Perhaps it is passed down the family. Apparently, some parents in China threaten to send their naughty children off to Singapore where chewing gum is banned. Lucy's parents, on the other hand, said her leg would wilt like an abandoned flower whenever she kicked something or kicked them in anger. And she wasn't allowed to have chewing gum even if she didn't kick anything or anybody. Her father might have heard about Singapore and its law, she thought. Just like him, Lucy didn't like being with people, because they could behave in so many incomprehensible ways. Like they would always stand too close to her when she was on the bus and she couldn't bear this 'communal intimacy'. Each time she felt crowded on the bus she would take off her artificial arm and poke her way with it through the crowd, tapping people's shoulders with stiff, sharp-pointed fingers. Then, she would quickly get off the bus and wave goodbye with the wooden offshoot to the shocked and perplexed passengers. These moments gave her inexpressible pleasure, because she felt she had power over them and she was the one to hold the sceptre – as she would sometimes think of her lifeless limb.

The knife stabbed the bag of mozzarella easily, the foggy water streamed out of the slit. Taking the white ball out, Lucy smiled with undeniable pleasure. She squeezed it hard and watched the ball attempting to come back to its previous shape. After looking at it for a while she started cutting it into tiny pieces at random. Feet are omitted, forgotten. Feet. Finding the essence of feet. Lucy put her foot on a piece of paper and drew the shape of it with the pencil. The drawing looked bigger, a bit clumsy, and it was missing the point, she thought. To grasp the meaning of foot, and find the right word to depict it. Yes, the word, the word, Lucy whispered, biting the pencil. The word that slides into you quickly and cuts like a sharp knife through a bag of mozzarella (like the word 'cripple', for example). Her mind teemed with feet. Pattering their own rhythm, or dancing in circles like the feet of a Gypsy dancer. Tapping. Tiptoeing. Treading. Trudging. Tangling. Twisting. Twiddling. At times she heard the loud heavy stamping of Dad's feet. Sleepless feet after Mum had left. And Mum's high-heel-shoed feet when she was leaving. And then Dad's noiseless feet. Hanging.

Lucy decided she would buy flowers for herself. Dad told her once that flowers always make people feel better. 'Feel better', a strange expression, feel exactly what? Narcissi could be good though, she thought. How bizarre that they grow from onions. People are like onions, truth hidden beneath hundreds of layers. They hardly ever shed the sheaths though, so you never know who you deal with. Some grow flowers and some make you cry when you try to dig down beneath the surface, Lucy thought and quickly scribbled the sentences on tissue. The florist's was just round the corner and she remembered seeing narcissi there the other day. The sweet smell of flowers embraced her when she entered the shop. She came up to the counter, glanced at the florist quickly and pointed to a small bunch of jonquils.

—'Would you like me to wrap them for you?' the florist asked.

Lucy looked round the shop ignoring the question. She wouldn't talk to strangers and would make loops around people avoiding contact. Scant body language sufficed, she thought. She didn't exactly remember what made her stop talking to people. The reason for it was probably creased away in her pocket. No matter. Stiff, numb tongue. Misplaced words are re-found in a multifarious expansion of silence. We shall be silent eventually, in spite of all. As silent as flowers, Lucy pondered. She jerked when the florist broke into a peal of laughter. His thin whisker-like moustache was dancing around his wide-open mouth, but they stopped moving when the man's face turned stern. His eyes were drilling through Lucy.

—Lucy, Lucyna... Didn't Ma and Dad teach you to answer questions when asked? Oh, they didn't, did they? They are not around, are they? What a shame, Lucy. Real, real shame. You're probably wondering how I know your name, Lucyna. Well, I might reveal the truth when you talk to me. But TALK, Lucy. TALK. The two of us could have such a lovely conversation.

She stared at the florist with dinner-plate eyes, her mouth agape, words trapped in her throat. Unable to move at all, she watched the florist coming closer to her...

—So, Lucy, tell me something. Do you feel so damn important that you ignore people when they are nice and they try to talk to you? What makes you feel so special? Is it because you look deform… I mean different? I'm sure that is why you've decided to get these flowers, right? Maybe I'll get a bunch of them, too. You know that your ma liked these flowers too and she thought I was special… Do you think I am special, Lucy? No, you don't, but maybe I'll manage to change your mind.

Heart tumbling. She could feel his wet breath on her face. Suddenly, he bent down and lifted the right trouser leg. A shapeless brown shoe was stuck on a shiny silver pole leading up to a set of hinges that were meant to imitate a knee.

—Do you like it Lucy? Am I special? Will we be friends now? We could swap our limbs for a day or two. Arms, legs, everything! That would be a real sign of genuine friendship, don't you think?

Trembling. Lucy stood speechless and short of breath. The smell of flowers made her feel sick, the look of the man made her… She screamed, she screamed loud right into his face. Twirling. Running out of the shop she stumbled, but she kept on running.

—You've left your flowers!

The man's laughter kept resonating in her head long after she had left the shop.

The mirror was covered with a thick layer of dust, but Lucy was still able to see herself in it. Her eyes were still swollen and slightly red. She looked at the stiff palm sticking out of the left sleeve of her shirt. What would it feel like if she could stretch her arms wide open? Would she feel happy if she could twiddle her thumbs, if her body was symmetrical, if blood ran down the veins in all her limbs? Reject the thought, your body is fine, she said to herself. Perfect asymmetry or illusory ersatz symmetry? Which is better, she wondered as she took her artificial arm off and put it on again. Off and on, off and on, off. She put the limb on the desk and started cutting the thumb off with a penknife. Back and forth, back and forth, as tiny pieces of sawdust quickly covered the desk surface.

A pair of red high heels advanced from the entrance door towards two worn-out brown leather brogues. Their tips almost touched each other. The brown shoes stepped away quickly and then again faced the red stilettoes. The thin heels went off the floor as the knees bent down towards a silver bucket filled with red and yellow carnations. Slowly the heels went down and lightly touched the floor. They were facing each other again but only separated with a wooden, four-legged block. Half a minute later you could hear the loud tapping of high heels echoing through the shop and then out in the street. As time passed, you could see some old loafers, new sandals, green moccasins or flip-flops making their way from one end of the shop to the other. This state of events would have been left undisturbed had it not been for a couple of pink deck shoes that suddenly appeared in between the others. They headed straight towards the brown leather brogues which stepped back a bit as if surprised by the pink visitors. They stood very close and it seemed that the pink shoes turned red. Now they were stepping away and towards each other, moving in circles, almost dancing, and then faster and faster. All the loafers, sandals, moccasins and flip-flops looked at them as if holding their breath. Suddenly one of the pink shoe soles started hitting the right brogue with such force that it lost its balance and a moment later the toes of the brogues were pointing upwards. Then a hand reached towards the right brogue and pulled it several times until it came off the wooden foot. Silence tightened around the shoes. It was only broken by the steady and slow patter of the deck shoes leaving the shop.

The room seemed empty. There were bits of paper and squeezed-out glue tubes here and there. On the desk there was a large glass vase containing the wooden limb. The thumbless palm was proudly sprouting four fingers pointing upwards. On the floor there was a big *papier-mâché* sculpture of the foot. Two curtainless windows were left open letting the room stare off into space.

Four poems by Krystyna Miłobędzka

translated by Elżbieta Wójcik-Leese

***

our now spelt with a capital letter
quest for the furthest into the rift of summer
a piece of sun on a leaf caught against our will
those random words, any will do, 'free golden'
our am on the verge of the lawn
vibrating touch of the hand 'so deep'
you think a well and your tongue gives it a lustre

you close your eyes
it will look

***

thanks to her whom he can see
through whom he can see
whom he cannot see
who is
from that far far away ahead of us
that opens for everyone into a different
meadow, differently green
(does it feel green to be grass?)
she the glass-maker, this rapt encounter
not to be captured

your childlike kite
a see-through tissue flutters down
into my hand

***

where do who do I
before I begin

who first, who mine, who best
which of my selves shall I leave for you for ever
why the one laughing with plaits out of breath
which myself shall I leave for you out of which deep drawer
in which photograph developed in a blur
the one older by you, the one silent about you
the one at the last minute running here

a face among faces, moved in a bright streak
with the eyebrows raised high
this astonishment everywhere out of place
on the shore of the sea, verge of the woods, edge of the bed
at the end of the tongue

***

with your hands to take myself out (to remain)
to squander myself (to have)
assemble me from the yous only, more clearly
I'll be none and numerous

Anna Bikont and Joanna Szczęsna

A Belligerent Voice in Defence of Peace, or Europeans in Wrocław

translated by Frank L. Vigoda

When Pablo Picasso arrived in Wrocław on August 25, 1948 to participate in the World Congress of Intellectuals for Peace, he was put up at the Hotel Metropol in the very best suite, where Hitler once stayed. He immediately went to Wrocław University of Technology, where hundreds milled about the grand hall, including delegates from Africa, India, Ceylon and South America (all in all, several hundred writers, painters, philosophers, composers and scholars from forty-six countries). All eyes turned towards the great Spanish painter as he entered in his colourful open-necked shirt.

The idea to organise a peace congress, in Wrocław (formerly Breslau), and to coordinate it with the major Exhibition of Recovered Territories was a true masterpiece of propaganda. In the Congress issue of the journal *Odrodzenie*, Julian Tuwim wrote that

> intellectuals from all over the world will see a country with their own eyes that without any help from Judas silver dollars coming from the pockets of bankers, oilmen and other rascals, is quickly and efficiently rebuilding itself, despite the vast destruction and plunder caused by the German fascists. Perhaps our guests will learn that there is a part of Europe not far from Wrocław, known until recently as the Third

> Reich, where a generation of Germans is growing under an Anglo-Saxon occupation, armed and appropriately trained, breathing with the lust of revengist war (...) The enemy is clear (...) Let our voices for peace resound belligerently.

The guests visited the exhibit documenting 'the accomplishments of the Peoples' Poland' and with their own eyes saw the enthusiasm these accomplishments aroused. However, it probably didn't occur to them that the principal attraction for those crowding the exhibition was the chance to see a tractor, something otherwise unavailable on the market, or to buy some ham, also not a commonplace item.

Polish sources credit Jerzy Borejsza with the idea of convening the Congress in Poland, and in Wrocław. According to Barbara Fijałkowska, a Polish United Workers' Party historian and author of *Borejsza i Różański,* the idea was probably conceived one night in Borejsza's office in 'Czytelnik,' and it was Borejsza's brother Jacek Różański, the notorious head of the investigation department at the Ministry of Public Security, who suggested that it would be good to spread the rumour that the event had Soviet approval. The Soviet Foreign Minister, Molotov, bought the idea and skilfully presented it to Stalin.

Borejsza himself told the French communist journalist Dominique Desanti that when he presented the concept to Andrei Zhdanov, the Soviet judge and jury in matters of ideology and culture, he was initially hesitant but then liked the idea and considered Wrocław the ideal place. 'Everything possible was done to create the appearance that this was a Polish initiative,' wrote Pierre Daix, then a member of the French Communist Party, in his autobiography. Yet he knew the truth. He was personal secretary to Louis Aragon, a French poet and editor-in-chief of the communist newspaper *Ce Soir*. Daix was in the editorial room on the evening when Alexandr Fadeev, president of the Soviet Writers' Union, came by to chat about the Congress; he was accompanied by communist-leaning Frédéric Joliot-Curie, son-in-law of Maria Skłodowska-Curie.

'I can only share my theory,' Krystyna Kersten told us. 'It seems unlikely the idea originated with Borejsza, and even if so, it must have been within the framework of a Soviet initiative to create a peace movement. From the archives of the Cominform (the organisation created by Stalin in 1947 in order to control satellite communist parties) we know that the struggle for peace was decreed a new priority for international communists at its third Congress in January 1949. Still, some secret activity in this area must have been carried out beforehand. The Cominform was just an executor; actual decisions must have been made in the international department of the CPSU.'

Tadeusz Konwicki who attended the Congress as Borejsza's personal secretary told us, 'today they say it was a KGB plot. I can't say one way or another, but I don't think Borejsza started organising the Congress with some perverted idea. It was an opportunity to show a different Poland. Instead of a country of dead corpses, you saw a country springing to life. At that time it was not evident that this would be his final chapter, that he would be soon pushed to the sidelines. I was twenty-one, his errand boy. For me to be at the Congress was an honour – luxurious surroundings, and celebrities all over the place.'

Then he started answering, as usual, in half-sentences – that he doesn't remember much and was not that politically savvy, that the most he remembers is the scene when Picasso took off his shirt (being two tables away). He added, 'it is not politically correct to say this today, but the world's intellectual elite was gathered at the Congress. I remember there being a festival-like atmosphere.'

Borejsza, who orchestrated the preparations, went to Rome, London and Paris to personally invite the important guests. When Dominique Desanti expressed her belief that they should invite 'big guns' like Sartre, Camus and Malraux to Wrocław, he would not take the hint. He already knew the Soviet comrades wouldn't buy it. Inviting Picasso and Eluard was as far as he could go – although they belonged to the communist party, one painted in a manner glaringly inconsistent with the principles of socialist-realism and the other had been a surrealist. As for Sartre, he was excommunicated after he publicly pronounced: 'If somebody asked me if a writer should give himself to the service of communist party, I would say, 'no'. The politics of Stalinist communism is incompatible with the honest profession of the writer.' He also co-established a new party of the French left wing, as an alternative to communism. The era of the 'broad-front' policy in which anyone who did not care for capitalism was potentially an ally of the USSR, was over. Now the party line, 'whoever is not with us is against us' was to rule for many years. This Congress would sieve out the undecided.

It was officially organised by a Polish–French committee. Irena Szymańska, then an editor in 'Czytelnik', who like Konwicki, accompanied her employer Borejsza to Wrocław, mentioned to us that this was probably the last international conference where French was the *lingua franca*. Shortly afterwards, Russian ruled on one side of the iron curtain, English on the other.

[Maria] Dąbrowska, a delegate to the Congress, after attending an organising committee meeting, wrote some surprisingly insightful notes in her diary (considering the times):

> Borejsza spat out a boring report and read aloud lists of foreigners, with [Jan] Parandowski and [Zygmunt] Szweykowski correcting his pronunciation from time to time. Outside of this, there was complete inertia. You just saw great tangles of teeth with tightly guarded tongues behind them (…) does anyone even think or ask what these 'intellectuals' would do if, God forbid, a war broke out? Can anyone imagine any country allowing them their anti-war stance? All these writers, poets, artist – if young they will be drafted, whereas the others will have to produce war propaganda. Scientists will be harnessed to work on deadly inventions, and this childish game for the 'defense of peace' will be over.' (14 August 1948.)

Still, almost all the intellectuals gathered in Wrocław had a sense of mission. The ruins of World War II hadn't completely cooled yet, and already the next war was being discussed, this time a nuclear one. They were convinced that their voices could tip the balance. They had already proved they were the conscience of nations. Like Paul Eluard, whose poem 'Freedom', printed on a leaflet, was dropped from the Allies' planes to strengthen the spirit of French resistance. The idea of communism captured intellectuals in all parts of the world (except of course the USSR, where the majority of those once captured had been murdered or sent to camps). Now they gathered together to appeal for peace.

The Polish delegation played no significant role, except for Borejsza who was everywhere. It was the Russians and the French who mattered. The French, the most celebrated of all the foreign guests, brought a spectacular team: Picasso (who had lived in France for years), Fernand Léger, Frédéric

Joliot-Curie, a Nobel Laureate in chemistry and his wife Irène Joliot-Curie, and – their glory of resistance fighters – Paul Éluard, Roger Vaillant and Vercors.

The Congress started with joyful meetings of old friends. Picasso happily greeted Ilya Ehrenburg, with whom in the twenties he had spent hours talking in Montparnasse cafés. And he finally met Manuel Sánchez Arcas, a minister in the Republican government during the Civil War, and now the ambassador of the Republic of Spain in Poland that still did not recognise Franco. In 1936 the newly established Spanish government had appointed Picasso to the post of the director of the Prado in Madrid, and Sánchez Arcas had signed the appointment (the painter did not make it to Madrid before Franco's army captured it).

In the Soviet delegation, Alexandr Fadeev played the principal role; he spoke first. Prior to him, the head of the Polish delegation Jarosław Iwaszkiewicz delivered a short address. Also, a short polite letter from Albert Einstein was read, but the appeal attached to it was omitted (the famous physicist proposed to create an international authority to control nuclear energy which obviously did not go over well with the Russians).

Fadeev first lectured the crowd on the contributions of the USSR ('The only reason you are not under the German yoke is because millions of Soviet soldiers spilled their blood for you,') and then moved on to denounce the sins of others. He spoke about the imperialist camp striving to establish reactionary regimes patterned after Hitler and preparing a new war; about American imperialists and their lackeys, who want to put people into shackles and remake the globe into one big police state; and about reactionary writers, those chain-dogs of imperialism. From the big picture, he went into the details. He attacked T.S. Eliot, in whose poetry 'the disgusting filth of human existence is intertwined with mysticism, hateful clashes with reason, and the propaganda of irrationalism'. He uttered that historical sentence, 'If hyenas could type and jackals could use pens, they undoubtedly would create works like those by Miller, Eliot, Malraux and Sartre…'

From then on Eliot became one of the black characters of Polish cultural journalism and literary criticism. Tadeusz Borowski wrote, 'the mad dog of capitalist poetry must be quarantined; alone it will die of convulsions, ahead of his social class. Eliot is a conscious *agent provocateur*, a bard of the obscurantist middle ages, a herald of imperialism – and an apologist for fascism.' Then Borowski charged that in Eliot religiosity is interconnected with racism, and freudism with apology of monopolies. And he summarised in a style characteristic of witch-hunts where the names of political adversaries are written in small type, 'his place is not next to Shaw or Mann. His place is alongside Koestler and Sartre, Huxley and Silone.'

When Fadeev delivered his speech, confused delegates looked at one another. Later Destani described the reaction of the French guests when they heard about Sartre, then an indisputable moral authority in France, being a hyena with a typewriter: 'Picasso threw off his headphones, Éluard slowly put them down and started scribbling, Vercors and Léger sat motionless. At the dais Irène Joliot-Curie and Julian Huxley exchanged notes. Borejsza looked like an acrobat cut off in mid air.'

The most daring reply came from the Oxford historian A.J.P. Taylor. 'The role of intellectuals is to perpetuate tolerance and unity, not hatred; whereas here war is declared instead of peace. Comparing American democracy to Nazism is not allowed.' He reminded all that 'it was the French and British who declared war on the Germans when they invaded Poland'. Nobody in the room, not even an Oxford don, would dare to say openly that in 1939 the Soviets, acting together with the Nazis, had divided Poland between themselves. Taylor also stood up for Yugoslavia when it found itself ostracised: 'Yesterday Mr Fadeev listed the countries that resisted Hitler. One country was left out, Yugoslavia, where almost two million people were killed. I cannot accept this kind of dishonesty.'

Another British delegate, the philosopher and writer Olaf Stapledon, defended Eliot and pronounced the sentence that set the record for conviction: 'I feel connected to the Soviet Union, but I also feel affection for America.' Julian Huxley, a biologist and philosopher, a VIP at the Congress and the first head of UNESCO spoke in a similar spirit.

The Congress was no longer nice and cosy.

'Fadeev conspicuously put down his headphones anytime anyone from the West spoke,' we were told by François Bondy, the long time editor-in-chief of *Preuves* (an anti-communist but not right-wing journal that collaborated with the Paris *Kultura*). 'Ehrenburg was visibly mean. It was hard to pretend that the Congress was proceeding in a cordial spirit. For the Poles the tone imposed by the Russians was a disaster. They had envisioned the Congress as a chance to maintain ties with the western world. Instead, in their addresses, the Russians heightened the differences in opinions between intellectuals from both sides of the Iron Curtain.'

Mikhail Sholohkov was present in the hall, but he didn't speak. The only trace of his attendance at the Congress was a very short interview granted to Leopold Tyrmand of the weekly *Przekrój*. The author of *Quiet Flows the Don* told of Cossack horses on the Don and their slender pasterns and long necks. Other Soviet delegates danced to tune of Fadeev. Wanda Wasilewska's husband Alexandr Koneychuk showed particular zeal. Fadeev did not utter a single word to the Yugoslav delegates; he treated them like lepers, which was immediately picked up on by the Russians and other delegates from the Soviet bloc countries.

Why had these guests first been invited and then offended? Remember that in 1948 the rift between Josip Broz Tito and the Soviet leadership was final (the Communist Party of Yugoslavia wasn't invited to the session of the Cominform); the Soviet Union cut off the supply of electricity to Berlin and blocked its connections with the western zones of Germany; a wave of arrests started in the communist parties of all the 'Peoples' Republics' (the peak was in 1949) and during the August Plenum of the Central Committee of the Polish Workers' Party, a witch hunt against the 'rightist-nationalistic wing' of the party began.

The address by Ehrenburg had the same content as Fadeev's but was gentler in tone. It was probably this ability that made Ehrenburg, the author of a few brilliant books (like *The Stormy Life of Lasik Roitschwantz* and *Julio Jurenito*) and several socialist-realist novels, the principal Soviet export to the West for many years. He propagated communism in a smooth and accessible form. His jokes were more convincing than many official démarches. 'What a lousy orchestra,' he would sigh listening to the Moscow Philharmonic at a performance during the Congress, 'if communism were really as bad as you write, they would have been sent to Siberia years ago.'

Maria Dąbrowska did not speak. We can read in her diary what she thought:

> There is little doubt that the Congress was not directed against war in general, but against the potential outbreak of war between America and Russia right now, when war would be inconvenient for Russia (...) This Congress is proof that Russia does not have the nuclear bomb yet (but I have no doubt it is imminent) and that is why it tries in every

> possible manner to draft all available resources within its sphere of influence in order to corrode war readiness in every country except her own (...) Fadeev spoke for an hour and a half like a pedlar for some company hawking its wares and slinging mud at the competition. The subject matter was no better than worn slogans found in any daily paper of the regime, the tone and the form were below the level of not just intellectuals, but of decency (...) only Ehrenburg displayed some rhetorical skill; he said the same things as Fadeev (he wouldn't dare say anything else) but in a form that was easier to digest and more elegant. He was just a better pedlar.' (29 August 1948)

Borejsza told Desanti, 'They killed my Congress. Is that why they came? They did warn me. They said, 'We will have to take difficult but necessary steps here. It's a swamp and we have to clean it up. We aren't coming on a conciliatory mission.' All the while I had been worried about what could happen. But not something like this. No one would expect it.' Desanti described the scene when Borejsza spoke these words of regret, walked away and then suddenly came back: 'But the courage of a communist lies in acknowledging that Fadeev was right. Leaving the ranks is easy, especially in the West. If you feel like a true activist, then stop Irene, who wants to go on the next plane with Huxley. If she goes, we've lost the scientists.'

Huxley, after delivering an anti-Fadeev speech, boarded the next available plane and returned to England. Professor Taylor went with him. On the other hand, Irène Joliot-Curie hesitated – to let the Russians persist in their follies, or give them a sign through a spectacular departure that they can't go beyond certain limits. Borejsza immediately arranged for a phone call for her with Frédéric Joliot-Curie who hadn't arrived from France yet. 'I am staying,' she said after talking with her husband. 'It is important for the final declaration to be balanced and indicate that the writer Fadeev was only expressing his personal views.'

Fernand Léger, already a well known painter after the war, having sent a wire from the USA to the French Communist Party to sign him up as a member, left Wrocław almost immediately after he arrived. On his very first day he asked for a ticket on the next available plane saying, 'I am having a crisis of faith.'

Pablo Picasso was bored by the Congress, but he marvelled at Poland, which he had first seen from the special government plane that had brought him there. He was sixty-six and it was his first flight. When the plane took off and circled over the fields around Paris, he cried out, 'My God, this is cubism, pure cubism.'

At the Congress he read a declaration in defense of the Chilean poet Pablo Neruda which included a personal touch, a rare thing in that room, 'I have a friend who was supposed to be here. He is one of the best people I know. Now he is hunted like a dog and no one even knows where he is.'

One evening when Ehrenburg was entertaining guests at dinner with anecdotes, Picasso turned to him: 'Admit it, you're bored to death here. Just like me.' Ehrenburg started explaining that he was used to this kind of gathering. Picasso interrupted him: 'Painters are to paint, writers are to write.' When the dinner was about to end and the speeches were to begin, one of the Russians expressed his regrets that Picasso painted in a decadent manner, typical of the worst western civilisation, and in an impressionist-surrealist style. Picasso retorted he wouldn't be treated like this by some petty clerk, and that he'd been called names before by the Nazis, namely a Jewish-Marxist painter.

Part of the American and British delegation voted against the Congress's final declaration, which was written in the obligatory new-speak. It talked about 'a handful of individuals in America and Europe who were greedy for profit and borrowed from Nazism the propensity to solve all matters through the power of arms, and who again are preparing a coup.'

Some guests stayed longer in Poland for vacations paid for by the Polish state. Irène Joliot-Curie spent time in the writers' hotel in Zakopane, as did Pierre Daix. It was September, and Bolesław Bierut had just become the first secretary of the Central Committee of the PUWP. 'I learned that Bierut had replaced Gomułka who admitted his mistakes and nationalistic leanings.' Thus Daix reconstructed his thought process after many years, 'I breathed a sigh of relief. Only in the Communist Party is such honest acknowledgement of one's errors possible.'

Western intellectuals flocked to the communist utopia like moths to light. How could such mental self-incapacitation (to use Aleksander Wat's neologism) of people living in the free world be possible?

The answer can be found in the power of communist ideology, a system that 'sucked in the best and sucked out their worst,' wrote the French intellectual Edgar Morin in his tell-all account *Autocritique* (*Self-Criticism*).

While infatuated with communism, Morin saw himself as a member of the apparatus sent to the cultural front. Like dozens of future luminaries of French culture, he was creating cohorts of lumpen-intelligentsia, a workforce to perform simple tasks assigned by the Party. He would receive testimonies of peasants and eyewitnesses from the Soviet embassy, saying that Katyń was the work of the Germans, and he would rework them into articles for communist press. In his *Self-Criticism* he describes the deceptive power of Marxist philosophy, his own delusions, the illumination and ecstatic feeling that the world can be explained (this motif recurs in many testimonies from both sides of the iron curtain). While deconstructing this self-deception, Morin traces the emergence of an immunological system that eliminated all bacteria of doubt. During party meetings, when asked about repression in the countries of the Soviet bloc he would answer, naturally Stalinism employs methods proper to the world of imperialism because it can't ignore what it finds in a world filled with evil and violence; it must digest it to bounce off it and rework it.

When one reads Morin's memoirs the most shocking thing is not just that intellectuals who lived in free countries with full access to information were so willing to believe any lie or nonsense, but that they acted out their own demeaning scenes from the social life of enslaved countries, such as endless meetings during which they hounded and outdid one another in confessions of self-criticism.

As for Polish intellectuals who sought their own place in the new reality, there was the fact that many of their European colleagues were believers in communism and that Stalin had a certain persuasive power. Jacek Bocheński recalled for us how important it was for him that when opting for communism he could think of himself as a part of European intellectual elite.

Marian Brandys, who after the war was sent to Italy by the publishing house 'Czytelnik' and the weekly *Przekrój*, told us how much that trip convinced him of the idea of communism. 'I meet communist senators, magnificent people. I saw Anna Magnani and Vittorio de Sica speaking in Rome at Piazza del Popolo, and all of them would say how much America wanted to dominate them. The only person who claimed otherwise was the trade attaché at our embassy. He would say, 'You know, they pump tremendous amounts of money in here; see for yourself what it will look like in ten years.' But then he ran away and took the embassy's money with him. Whom I was to believe? This just reassured me I was on the right path.'

Investing in the peace movement proved to be one of generalissimus Stalin's most successful ideas. The United States had the atom bomb so Stalin ordered the best physicists to work on development and do everything possible to slow down nuclear research on the other side. He was aware of the importance of public opinion in the western democracies. In the final declaration the Congress included a sentence about the free exchange of scientific ideas and discoveries; in reality this was so that Western societies be informed on the progress of their governments in developing the nuclear bomb.

In his autobiography, Arthur Koestler, one of those infected with communism who opened his eyes the earliest, thus described the turn of the forties and fifties, 'this was the time of the world movement in defense of peace that succeeded – under the banner of Picasso's dove – to convince millions of people that world peace can be brought about only by the means of the iron curtain, minefields and barbed wire.' The Wrocław Congress made the issue of peace a principal frontline, and hundreds of celebrities and millions of ordinary people all over the world signed the so-called Stockholm Peace Appeal which called for a ban on nuclear research.

Tadeusz Borowski was at the Congress as well. He served as the deputy head of the Congress press bureau and the deputy editor of the Congress newspaper (published in four languages and typeset in four different printing plants; the Russian issue in Legnica). In reality, as Witold Wirpsza who, together with Borowski, edited that paper, wrote in his obituary, Borowski was not just its editor, but also translator, proofreader and typesetter. And a carrier. He would drive at night from one printing shop to another; sometimes the car wasn't able to drive among the ruins; then, Borowski carried the heavy lead casts on his back.

Since then, 'the struggle for peace' had become one of the dominant motifs in Borowski's journalism. He urged all to sign the Stockholm Appeal, encouraged youth to compete for the title of the best young propagandist for peace (his appeal was mass-produced as a separate pamphlet) and lauded Stalin as 'the first standard-bearer of peace.' In his article, 'The First Day of War in Korea' Borowski informed his readers that 'recently American planes were dropping potato beetles on German fields' while the pilots munched on chocolate and chewed gum. 'What does Truman think about while directing bombers against towns in Korea, committing aggression against Taiwan and the independent territory of China?' he would ask. '...perhaps about the growing deficit of his government? (...) Perhaps he does not want to return to his little haberdashery shop from where, helped by a gangster, he clawed his way up to be a senator and president? Perhaps he understands that the sun of imperialism is setting and casts its last rays on the earth so tomorrow will be free.' After Borowski's death a draft of a just-started poem about the struggle for peace was found in his papers.

All the principal heroes of this book joined this struggle.

Jerzy Andrzejewski became the chairman of the Provincial Committee of Defenders of Peace in Szczecin and participated in subsequent peace congresses; he collected his columns and speeches resulting from this activity in the volume *Aby pokój zwyciężył* ('So That Peace May Win'). An opinion about their style can be formed on the basis from any random quotation:

> If the legendary monster has changed its name and today calls itself imperialism, and if it has a hundred bankers' heads, and the same number of heads of arms producers, if the ancient maze has become a field for preparations for a new war, a field of a thousand lies, provocations, blackmails and crimes both committed and intended, we not only must thoroughly learn the paths leading through this treacherous maze, but also illuminate them in such a way that no chamber of the modern monster remains under the cover of darkness or in a fake twilight (...) Allow me to lead you through just one of these chambers, the one that perhaps from among all the rooms of the Washington maze is adorned with the largest number of lofty feelings and notions, and sanctified by many centuries of tradition, and held in respect by many people from many nations – nonetheless, alas, it serves the same militaristic goals as other rooms in this gloomy building encompassing within its walls the entire duplicity and ugliness of the world founded on the power of dollars. The chamber I have in mind is called the Vatican.

The climax of the 'struggle for peace' was in 1950, as the war in Korea started. Wiktor Woroszylski wrote his poem '*Przyjacielowi z Korei*' ('To a

Friend in Korea') and Adam Ważyk authored the famous '*Piosenka o Coca-Cola*' ('Song About Coca-Cola') which was recited at every meeting:

Dobrze wam było pić Coca-Cola.
Ssaliście naszą cukrową trzcinę,
Zjadali nasze ryżowe pola,
Żuliście kauczuk, złoto, platynę,
Dobrze wam było pić Coca-Cola (...)

My, co pijemy wodę nadziei,
Wiemy gdzie sięga dziś wasza wola:
Wyszliście z Chin, wyjdziecie z Korei,
My wam przerwiemy sen Coca-Cola,
My co pijemy wodę nadziei.

You happily drank Coca-Cola.
You sucked on our sugar cane,
Ate our rice fields,
Chewed on rubber, gold, and platinum,
Happily drinking Coca-Cola (...)

We who drink the water of hope,
Know the reach of your power—
As you left China, you'll leave Korea,
We'll break your Coca-Cola dream,
We who drink the water of hope.

In the summer of 1951 Tadeusz Konwicki and Wiktor Woroszylski – together with Andrzej Braun and Andrzej Mandalian – were sent to the World Rally of Young Fighters for Peace in Berlin. Together they wrote a letter to *Nowa Kultura*: 'Hundreds of thousands of young throats chant 'Peace and Stalin, Peace and Stalin' (...) Peace is the most loaded slogan ever invented. On the surface a positive, joyous and uniting slogan is lined with hatred towards imperialists.'

Maria Janion told Jacek Trznadel in an interview for his *Hańba domowa* that for her and her generation, infected with war trauma, the word 'peace' (likewise 'socialism') was a magical word. 'Inside the mood of defeat we looked for ideals or words that would confirm that our existence made sense and show us a way of living. And we found these words (...) I was simply defenceless against these two words with their insidiously changed meanings.'

The above extract – its first appearance in English – is from *Lawina i kamienie, Pisarze wobec komunizmu* (*The Avalanche and Its Stones: Writers Facing Communism*) by Anna Bikont and Joanna Szczęsna. Warsaw: Prószyński i S-ka, 2006.

Two poems by Wisława Szymborska

translated by Adam Czerniawski

16th May 1973

One of those many dates
that no longer tell me anything.

Where did I go on that day,
what was I doing – I don't know.

If someone committed a crime
– I would be lost for an alibi.

The sun shone and set
but I didn't notice.

I have no diary note
of the Earth's rotation.

Would have been easier to think
I had briefly died
than remembered nothing,
though I lived without a break.

Assuredly, I wasn't a spirit,
I breathed, I ate,
my steps were audible
and there must be
traces of my fingers on door-handles.

My reflections were mirrored.
I wore something that had a colour.
One or two people must have seen me.

Perhaps that day
I found something I had lost earlier.
Or lost something I found later.

I was full of feelings and impressions.
Now it's all
like dots in brackets.

Where was I shrouded,
where did I hide –
it's rather a clever trick
to vanish from one's own eyes.

I shake memory –
will something slumbering for years
start rustling
from its branches.

No.
Manifestly I demand too much –
no less than one second.

Some Like Poetry

Some –
therefore not all.
Not even a majority just a minority.
Not counting schools where they have to,
and the poets themselves,
that's probably two per thousand.

Like –
but one also likes noodle soup,
one likes compliments and the colour blue,
one likes an old scarf,
one likes to have one's way,
one likes to pat a dog.

Poetry –
but what is poetry.
There have already been
several shaky answers
to this question.
But I don't know and I don't know and I hold on to this
like a saving hand-rail.

Three poems by Jerzy Jarniewicz

translated by Zoë Skoulding

Two and three zeros

Since early morning they've been playing Cohen on the Third.
Bad news. He must have died. Or brought out
a new record. In ninety nine
he'll be sixty five. Same as me
in two thousand and twenty three. Ridiculous,
these calculations, aren't they? And also
completely false. I've been calling you since yesterday.
No luck. Time to die or bring out a new book.
Millennium in two years. Don't panic: it won't be the first.
My fingers nervously repeat your number.

Nansen Passport

pour A. L.

Who told you, when and in what language,
that you speak a foreign language? A Spanish woman
from Catalonia? Or maybe the English guy
selling fireworks on the street in Edinburgh? Don't go away,
we won't be translating anything. I'd tell you
in Canadian that it's too soon but I can see
a bead of sweat on your brow, and straight away
my language is mobilized. Let's talk then
as the nationless: in the dictionary we have
Flemish kisses, Basque pinches,
Walloon whispers from ear to ear. *Lost in translation?*
You call my name in vowels I can't
pronounce. I compose you out of foreign sounds.
Je t'embrasse. It will remain so. I've banished the translators.
We're close if we are foreign to each other,
as tree and soil, as iris and horizon, as silence and word,
I finally meeting I.

Generation Relay

The Zdrowie pool is going to be demolished.
Grass will be sown. From end to end
grass. Is there another word for it? Because
I'd like to be fully understood.
Grass doesn't grow on cement,
I could say it in my own words
and so resolve uncertainties, at least some of them.
But you yourself must take the words to pieces,
the words in which we've been imprisoned. Go on listening
till you get results. As the time, so the language.
Don't miss it: there are changes at the back of the eye. We are
running out of orangeade. Those who come after us
will be drinking Coca-Cola.
Pust wsiegda. Let it be. Amen.

Post–Industrial

Photographs by Wojciech Wilczyk

Katowice-Szopienice, water-tower of zinc plant

Szczakowa, dolomite plant

Świętochłowice, colliery

Świętochłowice, colliery

Szczakowa, dolomite plant

Kraków-Bonarka, chemical plant

Adam Czerniawski

Not Lost in Translation

I think it safe to say that before World War II English-speaking peoples had no awareness of Polish poetry. True, a scattering of translations were available, but they were hidden in obscure academic publications and weren't very good. Here I offer my personal observations, mainly on the current situation in Britain. A full picture put together by a competent academic would of course include the United States and Canada, and it would need to cover fiction, drama and philosophy as well as poetry, for during the last half century publications and performances in those areas have also proliferated.

Hitler and Stalin, two great arts-loving leaders, helped bring about this change. Thanks to them, I and many other Polish writers found ourselves exiled in English-speaking countries; some of us acquired sufficient competence in English to attempt literary translations, often with the help of native speakers. Fortunately, a lot of Polish poetry composed during, but mainly after the war, was of high quality and therefore gained the support of such distinguished writers as Al Alvarez, Neal Ascherson, John Bailey, Donald Davie,Timothy Garton-Ash, Seamus Heaney, Geoffrey Hill, Ted Hughes, Tom Paulin, Stephen Spender, and others. It is astonishing that in Alvarez's *The Faber Book of Modern European Poetry* Polish poets outnumber those from every other country, including France, Germany, Italy and Russia.

Moreover, this poetry was frequently politically charged and, given the constraints on information during the cold war, it was therefore also seen as an important source of information about life and thought behind the Iron Curtain. Therefore money became available in the West for its publication in translation.

With the end of the cold war I considered it likely that interest in Polish poetry would turn out to be a nine-days wonder. I was expressing these fears in *The Mature Laurel: Essays on Modern Polish Poetry*, even though by 1990 enough poetry books and material relating to poetry had been published in English to fill seven pages of the book's bibliography, which now would probably be doubled in length. My fears might have appeared unjustified also because the book was actually commissioned by the Welsh publisher Seren Books, who clearly therefore considered there was sufficient interest in the subject to undertake this initiative. But not everybody in Britain was at that time happy with the influx of translated poetry from Poland and indeed from other countries in Central and Eastern Europe. Some British commentators justifiably claimed that the cold war encouraged tolerance of politically correct, mediocre poetry, lamely translated. However, it now is clear that good poetry in good translations has stood the test of time. It looks as if the poetry of Miłosz, Różewicz, Herbert, Szymborska, and perhaps a few others, is here to stay. There are several reasons for this optimism. The names of Polish poets now frequently appear in articles and studies discussing modern poetry in general or even turn up unexpectedly in commentaries not directly related to the subject. As I write, I see a quotation from Herbert in Garton-Ash's article in *The Guardian* on British intellectuals. Their works are increasingly being included in anthologies of poetry in the English language. There are now, for example, some thirty such anthologies in which poems by Różewicz appear. Other recent examples of how extensively Polish poetry is noticed: a doctor in America writes to me asking for permission to use six Leopold Staff translations in therapy sessions for his patients; a lament by Jan Kochanowski, taken from an edition limited to 400 copies of his *Treny,* published bilingually in Oxford – a remarkable achievement in itself – appears in Carol Ann Duffy's *Out of Fashion,* a Faber poetry anthology of 20,000 copies. Another Faber anthology, *Second World War Poems*, chosen by Hugh Haughton, includes not only works by Herbert, Miłosz, Różewicz, Świrszyńska and Wat, but also a prose poem by Zdzisław Stroiński, a poet not so far much noticed outside Poland, or sufficiently appreciated in Poland either; Lori Laitman in America has impressively set to music poems by Różewicz, and also in America Daniel Schwarz uses four Różewicz poems as epigraphs in his sensitive study *Imagining the Holocaust*, which includes a chapter on Tadeusz Borowski's concentration-camp stories. In Helsinki there is a megalith-type granite monument inscribed in Finnish and English with Różewicz's poem on 'Old Women'. English being today's *lingua franca*, the English translations are increasingly being used by translators of Polish poetry into Arabic, Chinese, Persian and languages of the Indian sub-continent. But perhaps the most extraordinary example is the inclusion of a poem by Leopold Staff in *Family Business*, the New Cambridge Intermediate English Course Reader comprising a selection of prose and verse. A Polish poem for students of English!

I have mentioned Kochanowski's *Treny*. Five translations of this cycle now exist, of which four are very recent, including one to which Seamus Heaney has lent a hand. But of course Kochanowski (1530–85) is not a modern poet come to prominence as a result of the cold war. My translation of the *Treny* was greeted enthusiastically by the late Donald Davie, one of those who objected to East European poetry being lauded on political grounds. For Davie, himself a dextrous translator of a 'reduced' version of Mickiewicz's epic *Pan Tadeusz* (1834), this translation signalled an affirmation that presentation of Polish poetry abroad can be detached from political manoeuvring, and no less importantly, that Polish poetry did not originate with Miłosz and Różewicz, but can boast a history of several centuries.

Peter Jay of Anvil Press, a publisher with a distinguished list of original poetry in English and of great Europeans in translation, including Dante, Goethe, Hölderlin, de Nerval, Baudelaire, Rilke and many others, asked me to revise and update Różewicz's *They Came To See a Poet*, which he had first published in 1991. The new edition appeared in 2004. But even more remarkably, Jay has simultaneously published my translations of Cyprian Norwid's *Selected Poems*. More remarkably, because as every Pole knows, Norwid, in contrast to Różewicz, is a difficult poet, at times very difficult. The difficulties are compounded in translation because a reader in the target language has to be persuaded that the difficulties, obscurities and idiosyncrasies he is encountering are not caused by the translator's clumsiness, ignorance or linguistic incompetence, but are an essential element of the poet's mode of expressing himself, which yields its mysteries only on close reading. That, after all, is what an attentive reader of Norwid in the original experiences. The book was published as a recommended translation by the Poetry Book Society.

Like every translator of poetry I am constantly taunted that poetry is what gets lost in translation. It is true that many translations fail for a variety of reasons, just as many original poems also fail. But there is no logical reason, nor is it a law of nature, that a translation must necessarily fail. It may turn out to be as good as, or even better than, the original. This 'Every translation must be a failure' thesis derives most of its persuasive strength from the indisputable fact that in each case the target language necessarily differs from the source language, and therefore no relationship of identity is possible. But absence of identity does not necessarily signal an inferiority of one of the two objects being compared. Moreover, the target language may possess attractive attributes which the source language lacks. I develop my arguments on this topic extensively in my essays 'Poetry Translation: Theory & Practice' and 'The Melancholy Pursuit of Imperfection' among my other contributions on the subject listed below.

'A Poetical Political History', *New Perspectives in Twentieth-Century Polish Literature*, eds S. Eile and U. Phillips, London 1992

'Writing and Translating During the Cold War', *Comparative Criticism* Vol. 16, 1994

'*De Amicitia*', *Thumbscrew*, no. 3, 1995, Oxford

'Polish Poetry in the West, or, The Canon That Fired Late', *Thumbscrew* no. 8, 1997, Oxford

'The Melancholy Pursuit of Imperfection', *Metre*, no. 5, Dublin 1998

'Absurdity and Poetry', *PN Review*, Manchester, no. 129, 1999

'Poetry Translation: Theory & Practice', *Modern Poetry in Translation*, London, no. 15, 1999

'Polish Poetry', *Oxford Guide to Literature in English Translation*, Oxford, 2000

'Como *Conversazione* on Translation' [H.M. Enzensberger, Seamus Heaney, Eva Hofmann, Adam Czerniawski *et al*], *The Paris Review* no. 155, 2000

'The Perils of Self-translation', *The Shop*, no. 9, 2002

(Ed) *The Mature Laurel: Essays on Modern Polish Poetry*, Bridgend 1991

Merryn Glover

Broken Bread

In the church kitchen my large pot of soup is bubbling quietly. *Kapuśniak*. Solid Polish peasant fare and a favourite in our family. Mmm… magic. Juicy chunks of *wiejska* sausage in sauerkraut, thickened with cream. Others on the team bring the main meal and the pudding, but the soup is always mine.

I was raised on the stuff by a Polish mother who never learnt to read or use weights and measures, but cooked with the intense concentration of an alchemist. She tested the oil's heat with a shred of onion before tipping in the rest, wouldn't add a herb or mushroom till she'd sniffed it and muttered over her soups till they were thickened just so. Everything mattered, as if she were stirring spells into the very heart of her dishes and the slightest imbalance of temperature or taste would render them worthless.

In Mama's mind, food was the only thing that would keep us. If not fed enough we would wither to husks and float away on the wind. Or perhaps, if the food wasn't just right, we might love her less and leave her. Maybe she hoped food could hold us, where it hadn't held Tata.

I carry bowls of my soup out to the folk at the tables. Here's Nellie, hunched inside an enormous coat with her shopping bags tucked round her ankles.

'Cold night, eh, Nellie?'

'Aye. It's a cold yin.' And she presses her lips shut and stares into the vacant air in front of her.

From all I can remember, though, my Tata loved his food. He ate each meal like a man starved, never talking till his plate was empty. After soup he'd tear up his bread till he had a pile of chunks on the table, then he'd use them to mop up the last dregs till his bowl was wiped clean. I copied him. Till I got married and my wife said it was a disgusting habit. Still do it secretly, though, when she's not around.

I give a bowl of soup to Wolf, crouched in his chair, tight-coiled like a spring about to snap. A vein pumps in his neck, just under the tattoo of a knife. Another bowl for his tagalong mate Ricky, who jingles a key ring in one hand and offers me a broken-toothed grin.

'Some soup for you, Margaret?' I say to the lady in a moth-eaten velvet suit with nylon hair. Her wrinkled face is caked with powder, lipstick bleeding into the lines around her mouth.

'Thanks, darlin',' she murmurs, and squeezes my wrist. Her rings spin loosely on her fingers, the skin on the backs of her hands shiny and spotted. My Mama's hands have always been thick as sausages and rough. She was an illiterate peasant girl when they came across from Poland, but good at coaxing life from hard soil. She dug a vegetable patch at the back of our tenement and fed us all from that. Tata got work as a builder and gradually learnt English, but Mama was afraid to go out. She used to send me and my sister for all the messages. To this day she only has broken English.

Food does hold me. Not to my childhood home, or even to Mama, but to this inner place where the sense of belonging is almost overwhelmed by the sense of loss. It's a tug of war, that only gets stronger with time. Just like the incongruous yearning to re-unite my parents. When everything else is falling apart, food sustains me.

'How's things, Will?' I ask the tubby man who's just arrived with his kid, Jasmine. She was a wee baby when they started coming, but now she's nine and all jabby elbows and sharp knees.

'Very good, very good, thanks,' Will says and bustles round with coats and bags.

I take soup to Shirley, who's sitting on her own. Her hair's pulled back tight around her head, laying bare the shape of her skull and the dark hollows where her eyes sit, bloodshot and half-closed. She spent most of last night showing me her scars and asking why God hated her so much.

'Thanks, pal,' she says, in that ragged voice, like the scrape of boots in night streets.

Why do folk come here? Yeah, it's a free meal and some of them are hungry and skint, but others have places to stay and money enough. It's something about the sharing in this food, night after night, something about belonging with other people who have lost much. And, maybe, just maybe, the food is more than memories of vanished childhoods and a time of love, but tastes of the possibilities of life, that here is sustenance for tomorrow, here is hope.

An old guy walks in who I've never seen before. Helping him out of his coat, I'm hit by the reek of alcohol, cigarettes and old sweat. His button-up shirt is stained and worn to a fuzz around the neck. Kinky strands of wool trail from the holes in his jumper, while his trousers are stiff with dirt and the dried-up spills of drink and urine. He's swaying slightly so I help him over to a chair.

'That's braw soup, son,' Margaret says to me. Tiny lines of it run along the bleeds of her lipstick. 'You make it yoursel'?'

'Aye,' I say. 'My mother's recipe. Good Polish soup that.'

The old guy looks up at me, his watery gaze unsteady on my face.

'I didnae know youse was Polish,' says Margaret.

'Oh, aye,' I say. 'Born in Białystok. Mama and Tata came over when I was three.'

The door bangs and two girls stride in, skinny hips swinging in their tight jeans. I head back to the kitchen for more soup.

Mama still sticks around home most of the time, still digs her garden and still cooks for five, even though she's on her own. Whenever you visit you get your plastic tubs of poppy seed rolls or *sos myśliwski* to take home. Don't think she trusts my wife to feed me properly. Don't think she trusts her at all, actually.

It has to be said, Mama's faith in marriage has never really recovered since the day Tata threw her out.

I take my tray of soup back to the tables. Two for the girls, one for the old guy, and one for quiet Dave, who has a Masters in French literature but also manic depression and a drug problem.

'I've got my ticket for Australia,' he tells me.

'Oh fantastic news, Dave.'

'We're getting married at Christmas.'

I've heard this before. Supposedly got a fiancée over the internet. A model with an apartment overlooking Sydney harbour, and he's always just about to go and marry her. But, actually, he's always here. And she never is.

What's worse? False hope or no hope? Tata arrived home from work one day with a woman on his arm. He rounded us up and packed us out the door. Just like that. Mama and the four kids. He literally put us out onto the street with nothing more than the clothes we were wearing. Mama still had her pinny on – splattered with hot grease from the tea she was cooking – and not a penny in her pocket.

We stood there with cars and trucks roaring past, the autumn wind nipping round our ears and my baby brother crying on Mama's shoulder. My little sisters were either side of her, clutching her skirt. Mama stared around as if she'd never seen this place before and then turned to me. 'Go and get help,' she said. I was seven and must have looked panic-stricken, because I saw her face nearly crumple. But she quickly looked away and when she turned back, all calm and hard-eyed, I knew what I had to do.

There was a man at a bus stop down the street and I just went and told him what had happened. He listened, his bristly eyebrows knotted together, then checked his watch, tucked his newspaper under his arm and came over. Later, at the police station, I remember the smell of my brother's dirty nappy and then my sisters falling asleep on the floor. It was deep into the night before they took us to a shelter with bunks and metal doors that clanged like a prison. I think we were there for a couple of weeks till we got a council house. When we moved in, the walls were speckled with mould and there were rats in the drains. But Mama scrubbed every last inch and gradually filled it with the smells of her cooking. Planted a garden out the back and grew herbs on her windowsill. It was home till I left for uni.

I sit down next to big Will with my own bowl of soup.

‘Where are your folks now, then?’ he asks.

‘My mum’s in Glasgow. Still in the house I grew up in. My dad… well, that’s anyone’s guess.’

‘So she raised you on her ain, then,’ says Margaret.

‘Aye, and did a good job, I’d say. Three of us got University degrees. Little brother is now a big-time financier down south and one of the sisters is a doctor.’ I don’t mention her divorce or his drinking.

‘And… the other one?’ the old guy asks. It’s the first time he’s spoken and his voice is a thin rattle.

‘She’s… ok. Has her ups and downs, but… she’ll pull through.’ I remember the last time I saw her. It was in the garden of the psych ward and she was planting turnips.

The old guy looks at me for a long time, his grey eyes pale as glass. Then his gaze drops to the bowl of soup and he scrabbles to pick up a spoon. It shakes in his hand as he lowers it, sloshing soup over the sides of the bowl. Slowly he fills the spoon and lifts it to his mouth. Most of the soup spills out, but he gets the last drops, clanking the spoon against his teeth. He closes his eyes and swallows.

For a moment he’s perfectly still, as if he’s stopped breathing. I’m just about to lean across and touch his arm when his eyes snap open. He struggles to focus on me, his brow furrowing with the effort. Then he lowers the spoon to the bowl and starts again.

Squirming, I watch him, as he slops through spoon after painful spoon, his shirt and the table around him splattered with soup.

‘Here,’ I say, offering a basket. ‘Have some bread.’

For a moment he seems confused, but then reaches out a withered hand and takes a roll. His fingers are yellow from nicotine, the overgrown nails chipped and caked with dirt. He takes the roll and tears it, the halves trembling in his hands, and then tears them again, and then again till there is a pile of bread chunks beside his bowl. One by one, he lifts each piece, mops the bowl, and pushes the dripping bread into his mouth.

I am turned to stone and turned to water. I see the smallest things. At his temple, the skin is frail and translucent, like a dry snake skin that has never been shed. Like a husk. That will blow away on the wind.

John Stape

Joseph Conrad and 'Poland'

Joseph Conrad's relationship with Poland is a matter of considerable complexity. To begin with, he never lived in or even visited Poland as we know it today: for almost the whole of his lifetime the state had only a virtual existence surviving only as a cultural memory, with Poland, dismembered in 1795, disappearing from the map of Europe until 1919 and the Treaty of Versailles.

Conrad's father, the poet, journalist and translator Apollo Korzeniowski (1820-69), sacrificed his life and his family to the nationalist ideal of Poland's restoration to statehood, keeping alive the notion of a homeland that had been divided up between Austria, Prussia and Russia.

Józef Teodor Konrad Korzeniowski, then, was not born in 'Poland' (as is so often mistakenly claimed), but in the Russian Empire, in the market town of Berdichev in the Ukraine, about 75 miles from Kiev. By far the majority of its population, almost 80 per cent, was Jewish, and in the mid-nineteenth century Hasidic culture thrived, its cantors famous throughout the region.

The territory had formed part of the Polish Commonwealth prior to the Partitions of 1772, 1793 and 1795, but for two generations prior to Joseph Conrad's birth in 1857, had had only a vestigial connection to 'Poland'. Ethnic Poles retained their language and religion but lived as a minority group among Ruthenians (as Ukrainians were then known) and, in Berdichev, among Jews. Conrad's relatives had lived in the region for two centuries, distant from the Polish heartland but maintaining their language, religion and ethnic identity.

He thus grew up in a multi-cultural and multi-racial environment, although relations between the ethnic groups were largely practical, limited to trade and commerce. His first experience of the Polish heartland occurred in Warsaw, in 1861, when he and his mother joined Apollo Korzeniowski, who had already settled in the town to pursue clandestine activities against the Russian state. The experience proved brief and tragic: Korzeniowski was arrested with a midnight knock on the door, imprisoned in Warsaw's citadel and in due course exiled to Vologda, in northern Russia. The Korzeniowskis spent a miserable time there with their only child, the health of the whole family undermined by the harsh conditions – inadequate food and insufficient heat in a ferociously cold climate.

Their psychological condition was no less desperate, the vain Polish Insurrection of 1863 bringing about harsh reprisals throughout what was once Poland and the suffering and death of several relatives. Ewa Korzeniowska's health, seriously impaired and aggravated by depression, caused alarm, and she was to live for only three more years, dying of tuberculosis at the age of thirty-two in April 1865.

Exile, the loss of his mother at eight, and his father's depressive personality and nostalgic patriotism marked Conrad's childhood. Mourning his wife deeply and identifying with the national dream, Korzeniowski became morose and possessive, clinging to his son. Given permission by the authorities to leave Russia for his health, he was unable to go further than Galicia in southern Poland, then part of the Austro-Hungarian Empire, where father and son first led a rootless existence in several small towns. Fearful of negative influences, and despite his rapidly failing health as he too became consumptive, Korzeniowski privately educated his boy, reading Polish poetry and French literature aloud with him.

In early 1869 the period of wandering ended, Korzeniowski and his son settling in central Cracow, where Korzeniowski again devoted himself to journalism. The respite proved short-lived, however, as his health continued to decline. He died a broken man in May 1869, his nationalist dream in ruins. Popular sentiment turned his funeral into a patriotic demonstration;

his eleven-year-old son followed the casket through the streets of the 'old royal and academical city', as Conrad later called it, then looking back upon past glories and uncertain about its future.

Conrad's own future was no less sure, and he now became the ward of his maternal grandmother and uncle, Tadeusz Bobrowski. Cracow marked a transitional stage, as Conrad later remembered: 'It was within those historical walls that I began to understand things, form affections, to lay up a store of memories and a fund of sensations' ('Poland Revisited', 1915). In a word, he began to emerge from his father's shadow and to live his own life, mingling with children his own age and discovering interests, particularly in geography and travel literature, both formative and important to his nascent desire to go to sea.

This next stage of Conrad's life is a crucial period of which little is known. He claims to have attended the prestigious St Anne's Academy in Cracow (where, as was common in the Austro-Hungarian Empire, German was a language of instruction), but no documents support this. He did receive private tutoring, and was also placed in a boarding-school for boys in Lemberg (now L'viv, Ukraine). A not very reliable report suggests that he showed talent for getting up little dramas; a no more satisfactory hint is that he experienced his first crush with 'a little Puritan of patriotism' ('Author's Note' to *Nostromo*, 1917). There were obviously concerns for his health, already somewhat undermined by the hardships of exile, and he and his tutor, Adam Pulman, a medical student, made summer trips to the Carpathian Mountains for fresh air and exercise, in an area famed both for its natural beauty and the efficacy of its waters.

During the five years following his father's death and his departure from Cracow for Marseilles in 1874, the dream of going to sea grew and then became insistent. Conrad argued with his guardians about it, in a kind of boyish way. Legend has it that he ran off to Trieste in an attempt to live out his fantasy and was dragged back to Cracow, but was promised that he could indeed go to sea if he did well in his exams. However this may be, he did convince his elders that the dream was real. After having his photograph taken, his uncle made the practical arrangements, and a tearful farewell with his grandmother and uncle at Cracow station in October 1874, closed a door forever.

'Konrad de Korzeniowski,' as he styled himself for a few years, was soon to become 'Monsieur Georges', enjoying the nightlife and vibrancy of Marseilles, and, within months, sighting volcanoes and tropical vegetation in the French Antilles. Wintry Cracow became a memory that steadily receded as other identities and other allegiances came into focus.

During the 1890s, Conrad passed through Warsaw and Lublin to visit his uncle, Tadeusz Bobrowski, in the Ukraine. In the summer of 1914, a family man with two young sons, Conrad saw Cracow for the last time, and was caught up by the war for several months, he and his family making their way back to England via Vienna and Genoa. Eagerly acclaimed by Poles as one of their own – the UNESCO application to give official recognition to 2007 as anniversary of Conrad's birth in Ukraine was made by Poland – Conrad himself stated to a friend: 'I am more British than you are. You are only British because you could not help it.' It seems timely in the year celebrating the 150th anniversary of Conrad's birth, to air and reassess questions surrounding his national identity.

Tadeusz Pióro

Lab Report

I'm suffering from lack of felt experience.
But music from the early post-colonial period
often helps, as now, with the Morogoro Jazz Band
playing to the rescue and experience felt again:
a snake on the seat of a withered Fiat
in a ditch, a snake in a chest of drawers,
a snake bludgeoned by the hotel boy
and its cut-and-dried skeleton bleaching
on the foot-path after lunch: beach-bound we,
bush-bound termites, and the lack of felt experience
burning like a fever.
Recently in Prague, for instance, I was
assaulted, insulted, demeaned, drunk,
pleased and displeased
and I don't know how that can be
so I'll consult a specialist with an empirical bent
to go with spiritual experience
or a clergyman who's seen it all.
I'd like to know why in Vienna
I was met with schnitzels and aspersions
while all I asked for was a waste treatment plant,
top of the line and full-blooded as a quarterly review.
But that's what we pay specialists for,
that's why they send us postcards
with wishes for the rest of our lives:

failed experiments must be repeated
in your own words, the sea captain
informed his parrot.

You could walk the streets counting dogs
or focus on just one breed,
frisk and prevaricate shamelessly
as long as you get to milk that finder's fee
and proclaim in another's words:
bull's eye, three points, oh, no, net ball, that must hurt!
That's the way to accrue experiences,
not by the pound but wholesale
and you can always spare a line for your pals
when the detective insists something
must have happened in Mombasa,
yeah, right, Morogoro, so the alibi
might not last till tomorrow.
At sundown the beach seethes with guesses.

Mythological

Today, let's consider the sun:
Will it shine in my pocket like a genuine coin?
Push metaphor past its possibilities?
Leave nothing for sale, but the body?
Will the patois of flowers be explained by coincidence?
Is weather the only criterion of truth?

Or does metaphor also conceal the truth?
Don't our senses deceive us when we can't see the sun?
You reach perfection only by coincidence
when your fate is revealed by the toss of a coin:
your thoughts turn it over like a dream body
that lies far beyond your possibilities.

Although what we call nature has great possibilities
common sense tells us what is not the truth:
tongue to tongue translation won't work with the body
even if the transaction is lit by the sun
and breaths' consonance, like a damp coin,
equates labour and wages, if only by coincidence.

Today, proper nouns sound like a coincidence
concealed in the shadow of lush possibilities
and necessity flees like an intrepid coin,
a dream of dawn or the naked truth.
If you want to wake up, take a look at the sun.
If memory fails you, subpoena your body.

Dazzled by freedom, you ignore the body,
for meaning, you say, is ruled by coincidence.
The course of history is marked by the infallible sun
the moon tallies other possibilities.
When you get starry-eyed, try facing the truth:
your promise of bliss is a haphazard coin.

When metaphor, like a worn-out coin,
removes from circulation its weary body
the tip of your tongue releases the truth
pure and sublime like the primal coincidence,
memory's pawnshop counts possibilities
usurers glitter in the blasé sun.

If the body excludes coincidence
and truth marks the end of possibilities
the coin of dreams buys love, indisputable and bitter as the sun.

Will Brady

The Bread and Meat of Life

Poland, 1988: Jan Grzebski, a railway worker, sustains a head injury while coupling train carriages. The accident leaves him comatose, and doctors give him perhaps three years to live. Nineteen years later, he awakes in a world he does not recognise. 'When I went into a coma there was only tea and vinegar in the shops, meat was rationed and huge petrol queues were everywhere,' he recently told Polish television. 'Now I see people on the streets with mobile phones and there are so many goods in the shops it makes my head spin.'

Grzebski's story is interesting because it reminds us just how profoundly Polish society has changed during his 'absence' of nearly two decades. Under communism, and particularly throughout the economic crisis of the 1980s, many of the things that we in Britain already took for granted remained unavailable to the Polish people; the state-owned shops lacked even the most basic of staples, and the population was largely denied access to the luxuries of Western consumer society. To acquire a car, or a flat, would typically entail a waiting list of several years.

But in 1989, just one year after Grzebski's accident, a landslide victory for the recently legalised Solidarity Party in the parliamentary general elections made Poland the first state in the Eastern Bloc to overthrow communist rule. This political revolution facilitated major economic reform, and since the early Nineties, Poland has steadfastly pursued a policy of liberalising its economy, making the transition from state-directed to privately owned market economy. Despite subsequent growth, however, there remain significant problems; decades of unwieldy economic structures operated under a tight central command have made Poland slow to put into practice the tenets of Western democracy – politically, economically and socially.

The parting of the Iron Curtain has had fundamental implications for the shaping of Poland's national character, and as Grzebski's unique case demonstrates, assuming a new way of life is a complex process. For those who remember the communist era (and for the one man who remembers nothing but), adjusting to this new mentality has proved difficult and sometimes bewildering. In the last century, Poland experienced myriad shifts: geographic (in the form of border changes), political (foreign domination and regime change), and demographic (ethnic cleansing and migration). Today, Poland is embroiled in a crisis of identity. Geographically situated between Eastern Europe and the West, and culturally between the Old World and the New, it is a country ambivalent in its political affiliations, economic stability and social values. Its people are divided – between an older, conservative generation, whose habits were formed in years of poverty and hardship, and a younger, increasingly exposed to a consumerist mentality that permeates every aspect of life and which instils a new set of values – and possibilities of 'elsewhere'.

The temptation to go elsewhere predates the dismantling of communism, however. In the 1970s, many family income providers travelled for work in Western Europe, particularly West Germany, to escape the constant economic and political pressures and the general sense of hopelessness. During this era hundreds of thousands of Poles left the country permanently and settled in the West, so that by the mid 1980s, Poland had become the major migrant-sending country in Europe.

Recent developments have galvanised this exodus still further. In May 2004, Poland was granted accession to the European Union, and Polish people the right to work in other EU countries. With the highest rate of unemployment in Europe (11.8 per cent in February of this year), and the prospect of better wages to be earned abroad, many Poles have exercised this right. While France and Germany put in place controls to curb Eastern European migration, the United Kingdom has not imposed such restrictions, and has, unsurprisingly, become the most popular destination in Western Europe for migrant workers. The British Home Office originally anticipated an inflow of 5,000 to 13,000 people a year, but by the end of 2005, according to Home Office statistics, 204,895 Poles had registered to work in the UK and pay tax. The number of unregistered Poles working in the shadow economy is probably as large. In Scotland, it is estimated that there are around 86,000 Poles, almost three times the official figures, with the highest concentration in the Lothians, where there are believed to be more than 35,000 Polish people living and working, with around 20,000 of those based in Edinburgh. Though exact figures would be impossible to establish, the Polish contingent in Britain now undoubtedly comprises a significant minority.

Most Poles do low-paid jobs in catering, agriculture and construction, as exemplified by the stereotypical 'Polish plumber'; 80 per cent of these workers earn £6 per hour, little more than the British minimum wage, but approximately four times what they could expect to earn in Poland. The financial benefits of working in Britain are not, however, the only incentive. There appears to be, among more educated Poles at least, a belief that emigration from Poland is motivated not only by fiscal need but the social perception of work there; that there is a pathological dimension to the Polish cultural mentality that does not reward workers with sufficient respect for their endeavours. The consequence of this is that Poles are attracted to societies in which a more established meritocracy operates. That is, societies in which wealth, position, and social status are in part – and in theory, at least – assigned through competition or demonstrated talent and competence. Over 4,000 doctors have come from Poland to the UK in the last three years, attracted not only by the higher earning potential, but also by the greater social value they perceive to be attributed to their work, and the opportunities for advancement. The attitude still prevalent in Polish society is at odds with the imported democratic capitalist ideology: a hangover from the communist era, which does not celebrate the flourishing individual.

An individualist ethic is perhaps the inevitable consequence of a capitalist system, or more accurately, a combination of neo-liberal economics and the belief, as disseminated by the mass media, of material consumption as the route to and proof of happiness. Nowhere is this symbiotic relationship between economic policy and social ideology better exemplified than in the United States, where the democratic virtues of individualism have been embedded in the national ideology since its inception, and material abundance has facilitated its realisation. But in post-war Britain also, a culture has emerged that emphasises the importance of the individual's wants over the social networks in which he or she operates, effectively eliminating the concept of the 'public good' (which hinges upon a policy of generalised reciprocity and community engagement), and towards a code of behaviour that engenders little, if any, obligation beyond the self. This culture has contributed to the erosion of social connectedness, and the devaluation of a currency which cannot be expressed or exchanged in financial terms – what sociologists call 'social capital'.

The term refers to the notion that social networks have a collective value, and that an individual will benefit from a concern for, and participation in, his or her community. Social capital comprises a set of attitudes and mental dispositions that favour co-operation within society, and equals, to put it simply, the 'spirit of community'. It can be seen as a resource, but unlike other forms of capital, is depleted not through use, but rather, from non-use. Social capital is maintained, or accumulated, through active civic engagement and social trust. Roger Sapsford and Pamela Abbott, in their study 'Trust, Confidence and Social Environment in Post-Communist Societies' observe:

> Trust is both a 'feeling' and a 'cognitive state': a feeling of confidence in those around you and/or in things unseen, but also the perception of socioeconomic systems, and relations as regularities on which one may depend. Trust is cultural, normative and deeply embedded in socially shared understandings… Simmel… points to the importance of *a priori* trust – the trust we are socialised into and bring to each relationship – and talks of a reciprocal orientation of people to each other, a concern for others at the root of social interaction, something implicitly presupposed in social organisation.

Traditionally an agrarian, socially conservative, Catholic country, in Poland emphasis on individual success and its material substantiation has never been a feature of the prevailing ideology. And while much has been said about the stifling effects of the post-war communist institutional heritage, we might also consider some of the social virtues preserved by the regime. Christoph Bühler and Ewa Frątczak, in a study entitled 'Social Capital and Fertility

Intentions: The Case of Poland' argue the following:

> Network related help and support is a distinctive mark of Poland as well as of many other Central and Eastern European countries. It has its roots in pre-communist times. Due to an underdeveloped infrastructure, a low standard of living, and people's orientation towards household and kinship, mutual help and support was a common strategy of coping and getting things done at the beginning of the twentieth century. This was also the case during socialism. Because of the malfunctions of the command economy and state bureaucracy clientilism, social networks were an important source of resources. In view of the perceived and considerable ineffectiveness of the system of public institutions under socialism, social networks played a basic role in determining opportunities to reach individual goals.

In other words, Poles have long recognised the importance of social connectedness, and have emphasised the resources available to an individual through active community participation. There exists still in Poland a notion of the public good – what Alexis de Tocqueville termed 'self-interest rightly understood'. One need only venture onto the street in any Polish town or city to see how this is manifest: in the proliferation of small, independent businesses, where the social exchange is equivalent to the material transaction taking place. The traditional *bar mleczny* or 'milk bar,' for example, provides meals that are cheap, nutritious and readily available to everyone. Consequently, they are popular among the elderly, pensioners and homeless, but also students or university professors, thereby strengthening bonds across the social demographic. As one Polish journalist writes, 'To many, [the milk bar] evokes nostalgic memories of those difficult days when people had to tackle difficult social and political problems because of the perverse system then in force but displayed great courage and solidarity in doing so.'- Though relics of a departed system, milk bars continue to provide a vital social function – this sense of solidarity – and encouragingly, these institutions still outnumber outlets of global fast food chains motivated solely by profit.

We in Britain have not altogether forgotten the importance of independent enterprise; there exist still some important repositories of social capital in our culture. The 'greasy spoon' is perhaps our equivalent of the Polish milk bar, offering unpretentious food at low cost, and attracting an equally varied clientele. But perhaps nowhere in our culture is social capital better preserved, or so eccentrically emphasised, than in our second-hand bookshops. Unique in their seemingly indifferent attitude towards commercial conventions, second-hand bookshops celebrate obscurity, diversity, and a shared cultural heritage, chronicling centuries of thought that might otherwise be forgotten. Virginia Woolf identified just these qualities possessed by our second-hand bookshops, in an essay entitled 'Street Haunting' and American journalist Christopher Morley gave them similar reverence. He was a great advocate for independent booksellers as public servants. The shops they ran, he said, afforded one pastimes as well as the chance to discover the 'bread and meat of life'. Edinburgh is home to more of these eclectic stores of knowledge than any other city in Scotland, and looking around the city's bookshops today, it is interesting to note the frequency with which they offer sanctuary to European itinerants: often their clientele, and sometimes their staff, comprise as diverse a quilt of ethnicity as the authors displayed on the shelves. Perhaps for those people arriving here from abroad, our second-hand bookshops, and other independent enterprises, in their quiet resistance of corporate homogenisation and bureaucratic protocol, offer some reminder of home.

The new wave of Polish immigration into Britain has done something to curb the trend towards corporate monopolisation in our culture. In Edinburgh, for example, we now have a vibrant Polish community concentrated around Leith Walk and Easter Road, where Polish-run grocery shops, restaurants and delicatessens are thriving; wander through Tollcross late at night and one is now often treated to a sensory experience that has practically disappeared from British culture – the smell of fresh bread, baked on the premises at the Pine Tree Bakery, run by a Polish family. Here, Morley's 'bread of life' takes literal form, and we begin to see what we have been missing.

The Polish presence in Britain is an example to us – of what we have already lost, and what we should perhaps try to preserve. In our increasingly consumerist culture, we have embraced a spurious ideology of individualism – to the detriment of our collective wellbeing. This ideology is malignant, and spreading now through Europe, has taken root in Poland. 'What amazes me today,' said Grzebski, trying to make sense of this new mentality, 'is all these people who walk around with their mobile phones and never stop moaning.'

Magdalena Tulli

Flaw

extract translated by Bill Johnston

And what about that other square, in a different story, of necessity vacated and closed down? And the suddenly interrupted threads of stories entwining it? And the inhabitants, removed from their own homes by a peremptory decree? Up till now they had lived where they belonged, uninitiated into the mysteries of the freight railroad, uninformed about the layers of sand shifting beneath the foundations of their houses, or the economies made in the construction of the walls, far away from the notary and his safe. They did not know the overalled masters and they did not know whose account they were paying for; otherwise they never would have resigned themselves to the wrong they had suffered. Misfortune is easiest to accept when it is beyond comprehension. And now, unlike the notary, these people no longer had anything to worry about. The worst had already happened. In the place where they had lived till now, the ground had been pulled from under their feet.

So it should come as no surprise if they now begin to emerge from the streetcar at the stop in front of the local government offices. First just a handful of them – let's say one family, like a sign that is a prelude to the arrival of crowds. Someone has to take the first step, and this first step is from a later perspective nothing more than the presage of an already familiar continuation. Thus, the streetcar comes to a halt and the first refugees appear on the square: a small group of dark figures of different ages, in thick winter overcoats, caps with earflaps, headscarves, mufflers and thick gloves. They tread unsurely, disoriented by the sudden downturn in their fortunes. The question of whether they may have come at the wrong time is the last thing they would wish to ask themselves. They too were not asked whether an explosion would be convenient for them. They hand down suitcases and bundles and arrange them on the sidewalk as if they believed – without so much as a hint of gratitude – that it had now been given over into their possession in return for the home they had lost. The streetcar cannot move on till they have finished unloading their belongings – till with the help of the children they have dragged out all the cardboard boxes tied with string, the sled, the teddy bear, the gramophone with its huge trumpet, and the canary in a cage. While they're maneuvering all these objects they have something to do, and while there is something to do there is also hope. Afterwards things will only get worse.

The moment the streetcar pulls away, they'll begin to look around helplessly, not knowing what to do with their luggage or themselves. They'll check whether they have brought the tureen with the gold band, a memento of the large service of the best porcelain that they could not fit in their cases. They'll have a slight quarrel, allowing their raised voices to drift all the way up to the windows of the apartments. Then they'll press their ears to the trunks to check which one contains the ticking dining room clock. But ticking is nowhere to be heard, so they have to open the trunks and make sure that the clock is safely where they packed it, wrapped in a blanket. If it hadn't been for the haste imposed by unexpected events, they could have taken whole sets of tumblers and wineglasses, and they would have had time to wrap each individual one in tissue and pack it in sawdust. Yet if it hadn't been for those events beyond their control, why would they have left home in the first place? The youngest little girl is hugging a small pillow. It is her entire luggage. She stumbles as she carries her unwieldy burden, but she won't hear any word of encouragement, because the grownups have forgotten about the job they gave her. She's despondent and she wants to return home. She was always the apple of their eye; so why is it that right now they don't hear her moaning and whimpering? She might be forgiven for thinking they have wads of invisible cotton wool stuck in their ears. When she stamps her little foot on the sidewalk, their gaze passes over her oblivious, wrapped in a mist of more important affairs. The pillow could just as well be lying on the curb, and that's where it falls. The little girl grabs at sleeves and coat tails, to no avail. Since her desperation remains without a response, she begins to understand that there is no return to what was before, and that all her privileges are gone. She sits down on her pillow, her eyes wide open in astonishment. The tears that proved useless dry on her cheeks.

But the two older children still suspect nothing. While the policeman checks their parents' papers, they will feed the canary with a crust of bread stuck between the bars of the cage, abandoning their luggage unconcernedly on the sidewalk. The canary, tired from the journey, ruffles its feathers and turns its back on them. The only thing left is for them to run around in circles. And so they run till they're fit to drop, laughing wildly. Gleeful at their own disobedience, for their own amusement they start running away from their mother and making faces from a distance at their father, who is walking round the square and, straining to be as polite as possible, which is understandable in his situation, is asking about a place to rent. The mother, in the meantime, is worn out. She sits on the suitcases, though she would rather have simply lain down on them. She is in an advanced state of pregnancy; her overcoat will not fasten across her belly, and she looks as if she could give birth at any moment. The children will keep hiding round the corner and coming back, hot and perspiring, until at the final moment, exhausted by their own giddiness, they burst into bitter tears. And it's plain to see that their laughter meant nothing, and that only their crying truly counts.

There is nothing to rent, nor could there be; each concierge sends the father on to the next building without so much as batting an eyelid. If only because of the cap with the earflaps and the thick winter coat, which smells of mothballs, drawing attention to itself and arousing mistrust. Otherness is always conspicuous from a distance, though it's hard to say how one recognizes it, if not from certain elusive attributes of cut and fabric. And what on earth kind of cut is that, what on earth sort of cloth is it, how can anyone wear something like that – such questions automatically present themselves to the concierges, and especially to their wives. As for the upper windows overlooking the street, not many details can be seen from up there, but even so the first thing that will be noticed by the concerned occupants will be the foreignness of the handful of overcoats, incongruous as dark ink blots against the clean sidewalk, with its pattern of paving stones like squared office paper. Concerning the matter of foreignness, then, the locals need only a single glance, accustomed as they are to recognising it in all its shades. There is no need for the mind to exert itself, and it's hard to be mistaken. The newcomers' attire does not blend subtly into the background; on the contrary, they are strikingly dark, and stand out in sharp contours displeasing to the eye. It can immediately be seen that they do not belong to this story. Foreignness, isolated within itself, is incapable of explaining itself, despite having introduced into the landscape a stain so disturbing it borders on deliberate provocation. Foreignness is foreign, and that is what constitutes its essence.

In the meantime, behind the lace curtains indignation is growing. If I am one of the respectable housewives following the doings of the newcomers from their windows, in my opinion the children ought to realise that they are not at home here. Because whether they feel at home determines what they are allowed to get away with. And if they do not understand this, the fault most certainly lies with their parents. The latter, however, are quite clearly occupied only with themselves and with what has happened to them somewhere else, and is of no concern to anyone here. Do people here not already have their own local worries? We have no need of new complications. And after all, it's quite possible that the newcomers, wrapped in their overcoats, scarves, and caps with earflaps, will bring with them a harsh climate foreign to this place: snowstorms or bitter frosts. One can only hope that if the threads of stories they have brought with them are immediately cut short, the newcomers will sit for a while on their suitcases and then, having nothing to latch onto, will disappear along with their luggage. They'll simply vanish into thin air, ending this unexpected breakdown of order, and the prior state of affairs will be happily restored. It's obvious, then, that they should not be given even the most cramped quarters to rent. Besides, for a paltry few pennies that may decrease in value anyway by tomorrow, no one will want to run the risk of problems such as icy drafts whistling through their apartment, especially since their entire supply of coal from the cellar would go up in smoke in the course of a few days. Why would they allow such a thing to happen when it's more than likely that the bad luck which has already driven these warmly dressed figures from their homes will continue to hold them in its grip?

Whatever one might think of the story taking place around the square, it was conceived as a light and smooth thing, and this fact bothered no one. It could have been told in a restrained tone of voice, without any trembling of the hands, without the need to touch on any weighty issues. Even if it contained a small amount of pain, this pain was shot through with comicality. And if a policeman appeared in it, it was only because of his amusing qualities – in other words, so he could strut about in his ill-fitting uniform. The handsome student was needed for balance, so the maid should also have someone to be sweet on. Everything was fashioned to a middling size, so there was no danger of choking on one's laughter, nor of shedding a single tear. The suffering in the story did not assume the kinds of dimensions that would exhaust one's reserves of sympathy, giving the lie to the belief that these are unlimited. Did it bother anyone that the notary pinches the maid, that the maid has a crush on the student, or that the policeman has eyes for the maid? What of it that the notary's tired, overweight body refuses to obey him, or that the student is shown in a less than complimentary light by the professors' comments in his grade book and by the excesses of behavior in which he has distinguished himself? What of it that the policeman, worn out by constantly being passed over for promotion, no longer has a heart for his duties, and contents himself with an outward show of conscientiousness? No one minded about the cream cakes in the glass display case, even if one or another of them turned out to be inedible. There were no complaints.

It would be best for the newcomers to go away again, allowing the continuation of a story to which they did not belong. But it seems instead that because of them, all local matters will have to take a new turn. For when the streetcar stops again outside the government offices, more and more new arrivals start climbing down in an endless stream, struggling with unwieldy packages and tugging teary-eyed children behind them. And since it had fallen to their lot to leave so abruptly, and they did not know if they would ever return, they had to put on their winter overclothes. If they had been asked about the smell of mothballs, they would have said they hadn't had time to air their things.

The windows of the local government offices would offer the best view of the scene below, with its ever-increasing numbers of dark padded overcoats and the accompanying bundles, trunks, and suitcases. The first few dark specks against the background of the sidewalk rapidly spread into a large inkstain. Looking down from above, one could see how many of the new arrivals were already encamped on the square and how many were still emerging from the streetcar. A trembling old woman is having trouble negotiating the step, but she has no need of anyone's assistance, since a first-grader in pigtails is with her and will help her down. Alas, there is no bench for the grandmother to sit on, though that is all she wants. A blind man in dark glasses taps at the step with his white cane before cautiously placing his foot on it. With one hand always occupied, he was able to take with him only a single small piece of luggage, which is actually just a violin case, and it would be hard to say what he packed in it – food, a change of underwear, or an instrument. Following the blind man, a flock of children pours out of the streetcar, black mourning bands on their arms. They jostle one another noisily. They're from an orphanage, which evidently also collapsed. The black is fresh in some cases; other armbands have faded. Each was probably sewn at some time in an impulse of the heart by a compassionate aunt shaken by the sudden misfortune in the family. She would have liked to be of more service, but she lacked the strength, and since she was unable to take the orphan in, she merely attached the child's mourning to his sleeve with black tacking, and so it remained.

The discoloured black moves no one; it becomes commonplace when seen on every second arm. The inhabitants of the apartment buildings have paused in their gateways and are staring at those who no longer have a home. It may be that as they do so they feel something in the manner of sympathy, but if I am one of these observers moved by their own goodness, after a moment I have to turn away in embarrassment. Sympathy that is utterly devoid of readiness to help seems to me discomfiting and unnecessary. It'll occur to me rather that my heart is too soft, that's the problem. Besides, is pity not pathetic in itself? Who is the pity for? For an over-abundant multitude in which each figure bears some mark of unsightliness corresponding to imperfections in their clothing. The idea that these blemishes conceal faults of character suggests itself automatically. The first impression is unfavourable. They are too big or too small, too skinny or too fat. The more of these figures there are, the more clearly the ugliness can be seen to be distributed among them in equal measure.

Multiplied by a sufficiently large number, the defects of appearance encumber the entire crowd like collective guilt. And the newcomers are as numerous as the inhabitants of the square; the latter will feel overwhelmed and powerless in the face of the distressing change that the mild morning has brought them without any warning. And they begin to fill with resentment, because they see that above all they themselves are the victims. The change has been imposed at the cost of space that is rightfully theirs. To say nothing of the fact that their flower bed, the centerpiece of the square, has no hope of surviving intact. But to the painful question of why the refugees are encamped under their windows in particular, there will be no reply. If this is my story, I observe the development of events with distaste and resignation. It wasn't the purpose of the streetcar to bring this wretched crowd. And now what has happened has happened, and cannot be changed.

The sheer numbers of this uninvited mass would have appalled the clerks of the government offices if they had not previously abandoned their observation posts by the windows overlooking the square. They would have watched the green of the lawn disappear entirely from view, everything blocked out by the overcoats – a profusion of dark cloth, black and navy blue, beneath which was the unseen padding, and beneath that the smooth lining. Nor was that all: beneath the lining there were successive layers of fabric, all the way down to fustian undergarments. The material made of different kinds of fibres disturbs the purity of the space – it is crammed together tightly in its excess, which accompanies the excess of characters. Under cover of an opaque curtain of mixed shades and textures the newcomers may well end up trampling the flower bed. Looking down on the square at the present moment, the clerks, and especially their bosses, would have had to ask the official question: who are these people, where are they from, and what ought to be done with them? Should they be dispatched without delay back where they came from, or on the contrary, should a room be set up in the offices where they could turn in their applications and be issued residence permits bearing treasury stamps and a seal with the national emblem? But there is no one left to wonder what should be done with the crowd, which has gradually taken over the entire expanse of the square, and is now sitting about on suitcases amid the lingering smell of mothballs, waiting for who knows what conclusion.

Ian Revie

Stones, Schchi and White Flowers

And we shall wither
When the song is gone – Gennady Aygi

The Russian vine stutters its last flowers across its green conversation
With the wall. Tonight the clocks change. The season of elegies
Entices as salt on meat. Off what shall we live but the stew

Of words and then those they inscribe? Wandering past Moffat
And its Devil's Beeftub we paused in light oblique so hands
Were raised at every other glance or faces starkly sculpted.

Schchi, I tried to tell you. *Schchi zelenye s'riboi*, I made it yesterday,
Like music makes the singing if you can find the words
Like the perch in the stream, the sorrel in the woods, lazy *schchi*

But the essential is the laziness – that's hard to live, although even
An idler can bring some stones. A cairn for a monument
Needs many hands and yours lacks none. The vine is turning

While you lie silent behind a picket fence and symbols
Of orthodoxy. Here are some stones that Babel broke.

Nick Laird

Everyman

The hellmouth, to begin with,
three fathom of cord and a windlass,
a link to fire the tinder.

An earthquake: barrel for the same –
we gathered stones the size of fists each time
and rolled them round in it.

Also, a pageant, that is to say,
a house of wainscot,
painted and builded on a cart with four wheels.

A square top to set over said house.
One griffon, gilt,
with a fane to set on said top.

*

Heaven, England, and Hell:
the three worlds we painted as backdrops,
when we left Norwich,

that winter so cold
the rivers slowed to silver roads,
and the oxen thinned to bone.

A rib coloured red.
Two coats and a pair hosen for Eve, stained.
A coat and hosen for Adam, stained.

A face and hair for the Father.
Two hairs for Adam and Eve.
Two pair of gallows. Four scourges. A pillar.

The Year of Our Lord I started the record
for the Coventry Drapers Company
was fifteen hundred and thirty-eight.

Autumns, we'd burn leaves
in cauldrons. In summer
straw would serve or bark.

If the fire wouldn't take,
a monstrous Dragon's Mouth
would counterfeit the way below.

Come the new moon from the velvet bag
I drew one shilling four for Thomas and wife,
and six pence for Luke Brown, playing God.

*

The Castle of Perseverance.
Abraham and Isaac.
The Judgment. Noah's Flood.

Each mechanical effect
brought bleats of sudden wonder,
the windlass to lower, the barrel to roll,

the link to set light to the tinder,
although no sound was quite the sound –
that catch of breath made by the crowd –

when Knowledge, Beauty, Good Deeds,
would take their exit left
and from the right, quickly, entered Death.

Paweł Huelle

The Bicycle Express (*for Ivana Vidović*)

translated by Antonia Lloyd-Jones

The attic room where Lucjan had been dying for a few months now did not smell of must or medicine, just antiquity. I knew that as soon as he heard my footsteps in the corridor he would immediately turn his armchair towards the door, so as I came in I would see his face, graced with a smile cultivated through long suffering. As I heated some food for him or washed the dishes he would ask me questions: 'Do you remember what the Romans called a side road?' Or 'How would you translate this: *Etiam periere ruinae*?' He was as pleased as Punch when I gave the right answers. '*Diverticulum*, as opposed to *via*,' I said slowly, 'it didn't lead to the capital but to a country estate. Like the one Horace was given by Maecenas.' '*Etiam periere ruinae*? I think that's from Lucan,' I said, as I served him warmed-up pierogi, 'and it means 'not even ruins will remain'.' Over the cake my mother baked for him each week, Lucjan talked about his final work. It was a commentary to *The Aeneid*, a sort of dictionary, in which he was making an alphabetical list of concepts that in his opinion were unclear, and had only ever been badly translated or completely overlooked by the Polish publishers. As we were finishing our tea, Lucjan moved his chair to the desk, where he showed me a page written in braille, cranked out on a special machine. I didn't know that alphabet so, lightly tracing his right index finger over the bumps, he read me his output for the past few days. Afterwards I would help him to get up from his chair, and we would stand at the window, where outside, against the rooftops of Wrzeszcz and some slender poplar trees, the clouds were drifting by. And then Lucjan would take off his dark glasses, turn his face to the light and say: 'Can you describe them for me?'

'Today there are some nice, plump cumulus clouds,' I would reply, 'but they haven't any autumn heaviness yet. It'll be a few weeks before they go grey.'

Sometimes, as I was on my way out, on the stairs or in the doorway I ran into Mrs Truda, who gave him his injections. I only attended this operation once, and I remember being quite unable to tear my eyes off her forearm, where a purple number from Stuthoff was visible. In the place where Lucjan had spent fifteen years they didn't tattoo the prisoners, but his skin bore a record of the past too. On his hands and cheeks – to his great shame in the days when he could still see his face reflected in the mirror – the marks of frostbite showed.

That day, when I was due to meet Fredek by the shipyard at four, Lucjan did not ask me any questions. He was absorbed in his own thoughts, and not even my news about the strike could restore his energy. Only once we were standing in our usual place by the window, where outside in the bright blue sky not a single cloud was passing, did he softly recite a line of Virgil with perfect stress: '*Ibant obscuri sola sub nocte per umbras,*' and then asked quickly: 'Hasn't anything come from Israel?' I had to sadden him with a negative reply, and I knew how greatly disappointed he was. When he went blind, Lucjan had donated his entire library to the university, since when we had been acquiring books in braille for him with extreme difficulty, because Greek and Latin, like Sanskrit and Hebrew, were an absolute rarity among editions for the blind. Homer was sent to him from London, and he received the Gospels in Greek from Los Angeles. Virgil and Seneca arrived in Wrzeszcz from Bologna, and he was sent a selection of Aristotle's works – by way of a Papal foundation – from Rome. Now he was waiting for a Hebrew Bible, which, like all the other major religious books, he already knew in the original language; he could translate any randomly chosen extract on demand.

'I'll write to Tel Aviv again,' I said in parting. 'I'm sure they haven't forgotten our request.'

The trams and buses weren't running any more, so there was a terrible crush in the local train. There was no other way to reach the centre of Gdańsk, and of course that was where everyone wanted to go, to the main station, from where it only took seven minutes to get to the shipyard gates. And either in a whisper or in a lowered tone everyone really was talking about the same thing: so far they're not shooting yet! But they're sure to start, there can be no doubt, the only question is when? I too could remember that December, exactly ten years ago: my father and I had gone up to the loft to listen for noises from the city centre through the open mansard window. The frosty air carried the boom of single shots, ambulance sirens and the rumble of tanks. The glow of fire shone red over the city. Now and then a helicopter appeared in the gloomy expanse behind it, firing flares, and then, in the brief flash of light, we could clearly hear two or three bursts of heavy machine-gun fire. There were moments when all these noises stopped, and we thought we could hear the shouts of the crowd repeatedly rising and falling.

'Just remember,' my father had said as we made our way down two floors to our flat, 'this is the beginning of their end.' Naturally when he said 'their' he wasn't thinking of the workers. A few days later I saw the burned-down Party headquarters from the tram window, once the curfew had been lifted. At the Hucisko crossroads, right by the tram stop, I found a shipyard helmet flattened like a matchbox. The stench of burning and teargas was everywhere. The food price hikes had been withdrawn and people were hurriedly doing their Christmas shopping. Just as hurriedly the portraits of the leaders who had been ejected from their posts were being removed from all the classrooms at my school. Our art teacher turned a blind eye as we burned them on a big pyre next to the school dump. Cyrankiewicz took far longer to burn than Gomułka, maybe because his pictures were on worse paper. At home in the evenings it was the only thing people talked about: how the workers had sung the *Internationale* before the Gdańsk committee, how they had been shot at in Gdynia, how those arrested had been tortured, how those killed had been buried on the quiet with the help of secret agents, how the Soviet warships were anchored off our city, and how on television the new Party secretary was promising the whole nation peace, prosperity and justice.

It was all running through my memory like a long forgotten black-and-white film from childhood. Now, as the crowd of sweaty people poured from the train onto the platform and headed in the hot August sun towards the shipyard gates, it was hard to imagine anyone wanting to shoot at this colourful motley of locals, tourists and holidaymakers, and certainly not in daylight in full view of the foreign journalists' cameras. Apart from the obvious advantage of summer over winter there was another, much more profound difference. This time the workers had shut themselves inside the shipyard rather than coming out onto the streets, and it was the street that was coming to them, bringing food, money and information all the time. At the shipyard gates, alongside bouquets of flowers and a Polish flag someone had hung a portrait of the Pope. The communiqués read over a loudspeaker sounded like a litany: factories all over Poland were joining the strike literally by the hour. The plaster Lenin in the shipyard conference hall was having to watch patiently as the demand was formulated: yes, we want a pay rise, but more than that we want to have our own, completely independent trade unions.

'So far it's like a picnic,' I heard Fredek's voice behind me, 'but I wonder how it'll end?'

'If they're going to crush them,' I said, turning to face him, and saw he had come on his bike, 'they'll only do it at night, when there's no one here.'

'Maybe so,' said Fredek, who didn't look worried, 'but first they'll have to force the gates with a tank. Then fetch them out from every corner of the shipyard. With a bit of passive resistance that'll take hours. But what if the lads set off a few acetylene cylinders? Or get on board a ship and cut the hawsers?' At last we had reached the fence right next to the gates and Fredek had parked his bike, leaning it against the wire netting. 'Besides, there's one more thing too,' he said, pointing at the portrait of the Pope. 'We've got him, and that's better than the troops!'

'I'd rather rely on a few dozen striking factories. And the ones that are ready to join in.'

'Well, it's actually happening,' said Fredek; he took out a packet of Sport cigarettes and we lit up. 'It's a real revolution, can't you see?'

Like this we passed the quarter hours, smoking and chatting, that was all. More and more delegations were being let through the gates, greeted with applause. Communiqués, committee resolutions, poems and prayers came pouring from the loudspeaker non-stop. And the mood of the endless rally intensified when a worker wearing an armband appeared from inside the gates: hands black with printer's ink, he threw leaflets into the rippling crowd. Not a single scrap of paper was left on the ground. Everyone wanted his own copy of the bulletin that the censor hadn't vandalised in advance, if only as a souvenir.

'Not a bad duplicator,' reckoned Fredek, 'but they're using too much ink, they haven't got the experience yet.'

'If only they'd read it out on the radio too,' I joked, 'to the whole country, don't you think?'

'We haven't got the radio yet,' said Fredek, having a serious thought. 'But have you got a bike?'

'No,' I replied, 'but you must have heard what they said,' – I pointed at the loudspeaker. 'At the committee's request the railway workers aren't going to stop the trains. So the city won't be paralysed.'

'That's not what I meant,' said Fredek dismissively. 'What do I care about the railway? I'm thinking of the bicycle express!'

And that was how, from Fredek's simple idea, my own August revolution began. Next day I called at the shop on Holy Ghost Street.

'They're selling like hot cakes,' said the salesman, smiling. 'Or rather we're sold out already – there's just that one left.' He pointed to a dark corner of the shop. 'Rather a clunky import from Big Brother, and I haven't got any spare inner tubes for it.'

Minutes later I was riding from Holy Ghost Street into Tkacka Street on a heavy but sturdy Ukraina bike, resistant to frost, cobblestones, rain, sun, sand and puddles. It had a very solid basket, a set of keys in a small box under the saddle, a dynamo and lights. Only the bell didn't work, as if something inside its simple mechanism was welded together, but it didn't matter. I rode slowly past the Arsenal building, the theatre, the market hall and the Academy of Sciences library, aware that the seat was a bit hard and would give me trouble unless I covered it with an old beret or a towel in the traditional way.

'Good heavens!' groaned Fredek when we met that evening on the corner of Łagiewniki Street. 'It's an armoured train instead of the cavalry! *À propos*, did you listen to Radio Free Europe yesterday? The Russkies are making noises about manoeuvres, saying they're hurrying them up and things like that. Do you think they'll enter the country?'

'They've been here for the past thirty-five years,' I said, barely managing to keep up with his nimble racing bike. 'Legnica, Szczecinek, Borne Sulimów, tanks, infantry, aeroplanes – they don't have to enter the country at all, they only have to come out of their barracks!'

'I meant crossing the border, an invasion, you know, all our brothers in the Warsaw Pact.' He changed gear and rode even faster. 'Like we invaded the Czechs with them in 1968.'

I had no time to answer, because Fredek was already braking outside the shipyard gates, where in the falling twilight the last of the gapers and trippers were hovering; shortly after, we had collected some bundles of bulletins from Mikołaj at the pass desk, wrapped in the *Voice of the Coast* and tied with ordinary string. Then we slowly rode abreast, through the park along Victory Avenue, continuing our conversation about the possible, or impossible invasion, especially with the East German People's Army participating, which here, in Gdańsk, was sure to be given an enthusiastic reception, considering the traditional Polish-German friendship; Romania would definitely not take part, but Czechoslovakia was sure to be forced into it, whereas Hungary's involvement – as we both agreed – was not a foregone conclusion, because as the Russian generals knew from previous experience, the Hungarians always sided with the Poles, just as we had fought in the Hungarian uprisings, so to sum up – we were just passing the Opera House – János Kádár could sleep in peace, though we couldn't say the same for Erich Honecker, Gustáv Husák and Leonid Brezhnev, that exotic trio, who might be joined by the Bulgarians, as the world's greatest Russophiles, apart from the French, of course. The tram depot, the construction firm base, the ball-bearing factory, then the paint and lacquer plant in Oliva – that was our first route. It all went smoothly and very quietly: at each gate someone wearing an armband collected a wad of bulletins from us, and sometimes we shared a cigarette, chatting about the same thing all the time – whether they would finally send an authorised delegation from Warsaw to start talks, not about a pay rise, but about free trade unions, which no one had, from the Elbe to Vladivostok.

Our night rides had no hint of conspiracy or special mission about them: the workforce in each place received bulletins from the shipyard via their own delegates and couriers during the day, and we only delivered whatever was issued in the afternoon or evening, so next day at dawn everyone had the latest information – the late edition, said Fredek, handing a bundle of news sheets in at the gate, the evening bicycle express!

Sometimes, when we didn't feel like chatting and we rode a long stretch in silence, I thought about Lucjan. He had just about witnessed my birth: in 1957, when my father brought me and my mother home from the hospital to Chrzanowski Street in the Opel he borrowed for the occasion from Mr Hoffmayer, Lucjan was waiting outside our door. Thin and haggard, in an old raincoat and a railwayman's cap, he looked like an arrival from the spirit world. His name had always been remembered on All Soul's Day, but no one believed he was still alive any more. In September 1939, when the Soviets occupied Lwów, he had been arrested and deported to an unknown place. He had not turned up in any of the Polish armies later on, not Anders' or Berling's, or in post-war London, or on any Red Cross list. 'He was killed at Katyń,' my father thought, 'or in one of the Gulags, like millions of anonymous people.' Meanwhile, here was Lucjan standing in the stairwell; seeing my mother's surprise, he took from her the quilt I was wrapped in and asked, 'A son or a daughter?' Afterwards, when he and my father were sitting in the kitchen, and my mother was washing me in a baby bath before the burning stove, Lucjan took a good look at me and said: 'Well I never, what a wee scrap of a fellow – where I've come from he wouldn't last as long as five hours.' I was to hear this remark from my parents many times, and for ever after in my mind his figure was shrouded in a gloomy aura that never lifted as the years went by. It wasn't to do with the facts that, though rather reluctantly, he did relate. That one remark of his contained a sort of grim reminder, a sort of dull thud from an abyss that emanated total and utter emptiness. Even in later years, when he was living in Warsaw and used to visit us every summer by the sea, as I became more and more aware of his amazing linguistic genius, I still kept running into that indelible mark in his personality. Perhaps that was why he rejected the job and translation offers that came with time. In Warsaw he was the bookkeeper at a coal yard. In Gdańsk, where a few years before retiring he eventually moved to our neighbourhood, into a small attic room with a kitchen, he settled for a job as a night watchman. In this final period he gave up the radio, didn't read any newspapers and even stopped going to church; he only came to our flat for Sunday dinner once a month. Once blindness, and soon after a progressive illness really had chained him to his bed and an armchair, he refused to move in with us, and gave any help a cool reception. Nevertheless I could tell he enjoyed my visits, perhaps for the exact reason that after coming back from hell, he had seen me on the very threshold of life. Now I was seeing him on its other threshold, the final one, and it felt as if we had both ended up in the same circle, but at different points along it.

A few bicycling nights later I visited him again. He asked me to tell him our exact routes. Rather than details of the strike, he was more interested in the look of the port from Siennicki Bridge where my chain came off; the driver of a police radio car who went past us had slowed down noticeably at the sight of two young men fixing a bike halfway across the bridge in the middle of the night. Were the tugboats at anchor illuminated? What about the wharves? Can you see the rust on the tramlines at night, or only in daylight? Those were Lucjan's questions, but when I read to him, one after another, the strike committee's resolutions, and then selected information from the bulletins saying that the whole country was on strike, or ready and waiting, that human solidarity had never been so genuine or so profound in our country, and that we would win, because after all one day we had to win, since we had always kept losing, at least for the last two hundred years, he just nodded politely and said: 'All right, that's all politics. But what are you going to do afterwards?'

'But you know that,' I said, a little irritated, 'I'm going to write my dissertation on Iwaszkiewicz, his Ukrainian stories, repeated and reflected Romanticism.'

'And then what?'

I didn't really know what he meant. What could happen then, except life? Marriage? Work? Travel? I had never lived in terms of the future, I didn't like projects, plans or specific ventures, because anyway, as Lucjan knew perfectly well, in our everyday reality nothing ever came entirely true, and at the drop of a hat it could all change, suddenly collapse, be destroyed, wiped out or smashed to bits. So how could he ask questions like 'then what'? If Lucjan weren't blind I'd have answered by asking: 'Do you think I'm clairvoyant?' But it wasn't appropriate for me to say that, so after a short silence I simply replied: 'I don't know.'

He looked worried by my answer. For a moment his furrowed face crinkled like a mask.

'I mean your dreams. *Oculos habent et non videbunt*, you understand? 'Eyes have they, but they see not.' Psalm one-one-five. Towards the end it clearly says: '*The dead praise not the Lord, neither any that go down into silence*'.'

I shrugged my shoulders. Did he mean my religious beliefs? We had never touched on that sort of topic, not even when he had occasionally explained an extract from the Bible to me because I needed it for an Old Polish literature class. In any case, I was already late. At the shipyard conference hall the talks with the government delegation were just starting, and I wanted to be there on the spot and not miss anything; the negotiations broadcast by radio could only be heard at the shipyard gates. As usual I left him the cake my mother had baked, and we said goodbye until next week.

The next few bicycling nights were warm and starry. After delivering the bulletins Fredek and I would ride to the beach at Brzeźno or Jelitkowo, and there, waiting for the sunrise, we would chatter away like souls possessed about what was going to happen – next day, month or year. Things that had been quite unthinkable for years on end now seemed within reach. Sometimes we reminisced about our school days, including the student chaplaincy on Czarna Street, where what attracted us was not so much religious need as the charms of the girls. Whenever Alicja sang 'Ma-ra-na-tha' from the altar in her beautiful contralto voice, to the sound of a guitar, a flute and a violin, there can't have been a boy who didn't want to take communion in her company. Joanna had a lovely black plait, and as she read Saint Paul's words about love, our desires, though not originating from the soul or the Scriptures at all, filled the chapel with sexual tension.

We had other memories too, of the city parks service and Scout Brigade IIIb on work camp in 1974, tidying up the old German graveyard. When the excavator scoop rose yet again, a white stream of skulls and bones had come pouring out of an enormous heap of sand – they were the SS-men shot by the Soviets, probably in 1945, lying in an unmarked mass grave. Iron crosses, helmets, and especially death's head insignia from the officers' caps enriched more than one collection of militaria in our city that summer. We managed to stuff our pockets and plastic bags with them before the prosecutor arrived. That same year, before the holidays began, Fredek and I had scrawled a message on the wall at our school: 'We'll get revenge for Katyń!' How surprised we were next day when instead of a maths test we had an assembly in the first lesson. Accompanied by two secret policemen, the headmaster threatened to expose and punish the guilty parties. Afterwards, as a historian, he gave us a half-hour lecture that proved without question that the tens of thousands of Polish officers and civil servants who died there were killed on the orders of Hitler, not Stalin.

At dawn, as the sphere of the sun rose over the bay, I was riding my Ukraina home. The quiet, empty suburbs were still dozing as I thought about that mythical journey of my father's, which Lucjan was so fond of asking about. My father had paddled an ordinary canoe more than six hundred kilometres along the River Dunajec, then the Vistula, to Gdańsk. In literally the heart of the city, on the Motława, he had put down his oar, picked up his rucksack and set off through the burned-out, silent streets, where brick dust and the smell of people burning were falling like a mist on the remains of the thousand-year Reich. He never liked to talk about it; all I knew, which was obvious, was that he had gone in search of a new life, because the old, pre-war one had ceased to exist in any way, shape or form, but why did he choose that particular route and direction? Only now, thirty-five years after his early morning march through the gutted streets, as I rode through almost the very same places on my bike, did I think he might have been like Abraham, who had received a summons from God: '*Get thee out of thy country, and from thy father's house*'. And if, I continued to fantasise, he might have been Abraham, I would have been Isaac, and then the remark Lucjan had made just after I was born, '*where I've come from he wouldn't last as long as five hours*' took on a completely different meaning and significance, it would be like a prophecy, not a commentary on an ordinary situation defined by history. But what on earth did that change in my life?

The bicycle express soon came to an end, on the day when Lech Wałęsa the electrician was carried on the workers' shoulders and declared the end of the strike. Not long after I got my first job as a journalist at the Solidarity Union information office. Fredek was in charge of the printing. The revolution was having ever wider-reaching effects, and for lack of other goods, had become the number one export item, as a while later the Czechs, Germans, Hungarians and Slovaks came to believe, and finally the Russians themselves. Whatever my thoughts about it later on, often critical, nothing could change the miraculous fact that it brought freedom, without so much as a single hair falling from the heads of our opponents – even those who had more than once fired, or given orders to fire, at people merely because they were demanding bread and liberty. In fact they only quailed with fear once, when the television showed the execution of Nicolae Ceauceşcu.

The clunky Ukraina went on providing excellent service. I rode it to work and to the university, where instead of writing my dissertation I was helping my colleagues to set up the Independent Students' Union. One October day as I was organising a rally, Lucjan died. The funeral did not draw a crowd. A few old men – former Gulag prisoners, the priest, my parents and I said the prayers. The day before the burial, when Lucjan's body was lying in the mortuary, my father and I went to his attic to sort out his flat a bit. In the letter box I found a delivery note, and that afternoon I collected the parcel. It was the Hebrew Bible, published by the Landau Foundation, if I remember rightly.

'What shall we do with it now?' my mother fretted. 'They don't keep braille in normal libraries, and I'm sure no one knows Hebrew at the ones for the blind!'

'We'd best send it back,' my father reckoned.

But I had another idea. In the chapel at Srebrzysko, before the coffin was closed, I placed the Book in Lucjan's hands, with his right index finger just under the cover, touching the first letter of Bereshit, or the Book of Genesis. As the gravediggers were flattening the small mound of earth with their spades, I remembered a line from *The Aeneid* that I had heard my cousin Lucjan quote in the first days of the August strike: *Ibant obscuri sola sub nocte per umbras*. Distracted by the funeral, for lack of a dictionary I couldn't translate it properly, and afterwards I plain forgot about it. Years later, as I was leafing through a beautiful translation of Virgil in a bookshop, I found that extract, which goes: 'On they went, those dim travellers under the lonely night, through gloom…'

Polish Shops in Edinburgh

Photographs by Desirée Elfström

Polskie Delikatesy U Gigusia

Polish Delikatessen

Neptun Polish Food

Pine Tree Bakery

Deli Polonia

Rock 'n' Roll Tattoo and Piercing

Dilys Rose

Olga's Back

As soon as her country became a nation state
of Europe she upped and left, rucksack full
of clothes for all occasions. No-one wept.
People rejoiced in their new-found licence
to scatter unhindered across the map;
remembered when leavetakings were hushed
and anxious, conducted in the dead of night;
gave thanks that their days of scaling walls
and snipping barbed wire fences were over.
Now we can visit whenever we like!
Still, they pressed her to take a salty cheese,
a sausage, painted eggs, the address of a cousin
no-one had heard from in fifty years.
If you see him, tell him it's time he came home.

In the city where, through World War II,
grandfather studied medicine, she rents a room;
it's drab and cramped but all her own
and nobody's taking notes behind the wall.
She finds a job, makes friends, practises
the language, learns its jokes, its idiom,
its ways with praise and insult. As yet,
guys can't place her accent but find it sexy.
When she invites one back for coffee/vodka,
she makes the usual kind of conversation
until, predictably, he asks where she's from.
Lowering the waistband of her jeans,
she reveals the neat blue trademark,
tattooed on her back: *Made in Poland.*

Elżbieta Wójcik-Leese

Just Did It
Four Poetry Nominations

NIKE. Nowadays associated with the sportswear mogul, commercials featuring athletes in action and the slogan: 'Just do it.' Nike. In ancient times revered as the goddess of victory, who helped Zeus to win the war against the Titans. This winged young woman carrying a laurel or a palm branch came to symbolise not only victory in battle, but success in sporting rivalry, beauty contests as well as music and craft competitions. 'Nike.' For over a decade Poland's most prestigious literary award for poetry, fiction, essays, memoirs, reportage and criticism. The winner receives a statuette: two wings unfurled skywards, with one feather – a quill – boisterously at an angle.

Past winners have included Czesław Miłosz, Tadeusz Różewicz and Stanisław Barańczak (known to English-speaking readers also as the translator of Wisława Szymborska and, with Seamus Heaney, of Jan Kochanowski's *Laments*). Fiction writers who can boast this laurel and whose work has been translated into English are Jerzy Pilch, Andrzej Stasiuk and Dorota Masłowska.

On the first Sunday of October, the eleventh winner will be announced during a televised ceremony. This year four poetry books have been nominated: *Drzazga* (Splinter) by Ewa Lipska, *Pełne Morze* (High Seas) by Wojciech Bonowicz, *Muzyka środka* (Mainstream Music of the Interior) by

Marcin Świetlicki and *Kolonie* (Colonies) by Tomasz Różycki.

Ewa Lipska's two previous collections, *Ja* (I) and *Gdzie indziej* (Elsewhere), have also been distinguished by a 'Nike' nomination. Their author (b. 1945), who lives in Kraków and used to work at the Polish Embassy in Vienna, would gladly embrace the ironies and nuances of the dual Nike/NIKE, this hybrid epitome of our penchant for mixing high and low culture. Lipska's poetic diction abounds in such deliberate unions of the sophisticated and mundane, the elegant and stark plain. In her poems, fate, chance, death, love – the universal themes of humanity – co-exist with McDonald's, hip-hop or easyJet. 'My poems change, the way our world does. Although I don't approve of it all, I don't quarrel with it, I don't feel bitter about it... I don't negate novelties, my poems swarm with them: texting, the internet,' Lipska emphasises her interest in the changing realities of our life and the languages – rather than one language – we employ and constantly modify to talk about them.

Splinter (Wydawnictwo Literackie) contains twenty-one poems composed over several months in 2005: testimonies to visual, aural and cognitive attentiveness. This poetic diary-cum-journal both captures and transcends its immediate circumstances. The described moments and observations, usually expressed in couplets, are threaded together paratactically (often with conjunctions missing) in a string of conceptual beads. In Lipska's poems, detail reveals its opalescence: milky white or colourless, it seems to change in hue according to its surroundings. It proves its attractiveness in a witty remark, a nostalgic observation or a jocular comment, aspiring to aphoristic wisdom, melancholic tone and wry humour.

Such surroundings favourable to our careful considerations are created not only by the formal arrangements of lines, stanzas and poems, but also by the white of the blank pages facing the poems to their left. At the bottom of each blank page a magnified black-and-white image of splinter points its sharper end at the poem opposite. This chipped-off piece of a larger whole can become extremely bothersome, signalling its presence with discomfort and pain: 'It's difficult to take out,/ even more difficult to describe,' says Lipska in the title poem of the volume, which opens with a confession from a young poetry apprentice to the more experienced poet: 'I like you.' With characteristic maturity of judgement and metaphoric inventiveness Lipska calls him 'A novice carpenter of words,' and employs the language and images of carpentry to write about another craft: poetry. The 'ambitious noise' of 'the literary lumber mill' accompanies our efforts to acquire the mastery of language, which frequently fails us. 'The apprentices veneer the gullible tongue,' they cut and chisel, trim and plane. What hinders our work, but, paradoxically, compels us to try harder, is a splinter, sticking in our memory, festering, impossible to ignore. 'Wood shavings are flying. Stubs of angels./ Dust all the way up to heaven.'

The conclusion of the title poem illustrates Lipska's typical strategy of breaking apart words conventionally set together; of revitalising associations by juxtaposing disparate cognitive domains ('cables of leaves', 'allergic walls', 'summer from the Polish grill'); of reaching other levels of meaning by metaphorically extending the lexicon. Here the rumbling car and its driver impersonate a married couple; a married couple who live at the chemist's write each other letter-prescriptions and wake up to the 'fizzy tablet of dawn'; at Christmas sleet gathers round the table, instead of relatives; and the Live Update cannot secure immortality.

Between the untitled quatrain opening the book almost like its motto:

***

It's worth dying
for such a poem
which
cannot be trusted by death

and the final poem, 'The Dead End,' Lipska inserts other meditations on 'the ageing future tense' as well as blossoming absences. Yet it is not the tone of bereavement or quiet resignation that dominates *Splinter*, but rather the good-humoured acceptance of things passing and the belief that the poet 'bequeaths to you/ a spare reality,' even while she is waving her last will.

The last rites of passage, or, more precisely, the rites of our human last passages are at the centre of *High Seas* (Biuro Literackie) by Wojciech Bonowicz – as is our need to comprehend what escapes our understanding: history, destiny, God, evil, death, forgiveness or affection. Bonowicz (b. 1967), a Polish literature graduate and editor of the Kraków-based monthly *Znak*, which is concerned with religion, philosophy and culture, feels equally at home when writing about the Hesperides, the fortunate isles of Greek mythology, Celan, contemporary Polish politics, war refugees, Christ or flying on an aeroplane. He does not shy away from big words and themes, although his poems do not have epic ambitions. They hint, suggest, sketch a picture and withdraw before too much is recounted. They do not offer solutions, they do not disperse doubts by reaching some satisfactory punchline. Instead, through ellipsis and understatement, they invite questions and silence. 'The point is not to fall silent completely,' explains the poet, 'but to write a text which would "summon" silence, lead beyond itself, open up… it's like a prayer. Although you say something, the words are not the most important. Rather, with the help of the words you want to create a space, a place, a vessel which will fill up with silence, with the unknown. You can specify the unknown, call it love, God, the Other, but you can never state beyond doubt: that's this and only this. Because there's always something else.'

This belief in something else always there prevents Bonowicz from becoming just a religious poet, or a philosophical poet, or a meditative poet, or a parabolic poet. The readiness to remain open allows him to constantly rehearse, extend and revise his own ideas as well as those of others. One conviction, however, remains constant: that a poem is a song, not so much a lyric song, more akin to a chorus in ancient Greek drama, commenting on the action deemed significant at this particular moment. It may become a song of testimony, fear, or justice, but one thing is certain: 'the dry eye of the song' will doggedly follow the events and their protagonists. Under its merciless scrutiny, divine heroes become more human. God, 'tender and weak with love,' fits more our 'silly human dream':

He tiptoes into the room and tucks me in.
His body is full of thorns. His sweat dense and sweet.

Such disturbing realisations of the co-existence of opposites (when, for example, God and his eternal adversary are spotted working together) may suggest that 'the language of revelation clouds like water under cut flowers'. More probably, however, they will show that 'at the rise of the sun the world adheres to me' and this rather odd graft may prove our complex humanity, where evil can be transcended by empathy.

The mind is its own place, and in itself
Can make a Heaven of Hell, a Hell of Heaven.

Thus spoke Satan in Milton's *Paradise Lost*, offering his fiendishly convoluted argument, at the same time intimating one of the difficult truths about man. Marcin Świetlicki's 'satans' (meaningfully, though unconventionally, in the plural) do not resemble oriental despots traversing the nine spheres of the created cosmos. Disturbingly familiar, they inhabit our domestic, innermost spaces. *Mainstream Music of the Interior* (Wydawnictwo a5) explores these territories, where night carries 'a seed of hell' that needs to be treated with sleep and dreams. Świetlicki's speaker – occasionally referred to as 'Świetlicki' or 'Marcin' in a gesture of subversive self-concentration that is far from autobiography – follows the route of 'sen', which in Polish means both sleep and dream. He listens to how 'night expresses itself'. The trouble is that the Polish originals take advantage not only of the dual meaning of 'sen', but also of 'wyrażać się': to express oneself as well as to curse.

More recent poetry by Marcin Świetlicki (b. 1961), nominated for 'Nike' for *Pieśni profana* (Songs of the Profaner, 1998) and shortlisted for *Czynny do odwołania* (Unclosed Until Further Notice, 2001), examines conceptual as well as linguistic coincidences and co-occurences, unsettling various received notions. The title of the 2006 volume, *Muzyka środka*, uses the popular concept of 'mainstream music' (it's worth remembering that Świetlicki is an experimental musician and performer of his own poems) to suggest not only the golden mean, a middle ground between the extremes (his writing has a notoriously rebellious streak), but also the interior, the innermost. Therefore the opening poem, 'Świetlicki – Reactivated', which deliberately refers us to *The Matrix*, describes how 'the persona scrambles out from nowhere into the daylight/ to frighten others with his return.' This comeback, the emergence from the dark pit (Milton's 'abortive gulf') into light, signals the upset axiology of Świetlicki's exploration: darkness and light, sleep and the appearance of life are far from being unequivocally negative or positive.

It cost a lot. The Promised Land
has already been prodded by
enemies. We must
proceed without light.

'What in me is dark/ Illumine; what is low, raise and support,' Milton invoked his muse, and Świetlicki sends his protagonist, called 'Master,' on a rambling walk through the city in a hellishly monotonous, wintry March. The walk takes him to 'Hotel Limbus. Numer 12/13,' the contemporary

Polish equivalent of Dante's Limbo and Milton's Paradise of Fools.

All th' unaccomplished works of nature's hand,
Abortive, monstrous or unkindly mixed,
Dissolved on earth, fleet hither, and in vain,
Till final dissolution wander here.

Instead of dissolution, Świetlicki's long prose poem offers a resolution that undercuts the epic dimensions of the main hero:

Master made one step towards light.

Then one step back.
Towards darkness.

Then two steps towards light.
And then he turned round and almost running, through the darkness, returned home.

He took the bitch for a walk, it was the time.
High time.

The absurdity of the clash between his anxious hesitation and the purposefulness of walking the dog (the bitch, rather), because the right, long-awaited moment has come, reveals the tragic heroism of an ordinary man.

In me, too, there's darkness, a little light;
black footprints which I leave on white surfaces.

The speaker is no longer Świetlicki's protagonist, but the mental traveller of Tomasz Różycki's *Colonies* (Znak) on his voyage across seventy-seven French sonnets to the other side: of this world, of another world, of some world to be yet discovered and colonised by writing. The poems, numbered and dated, constitute a log: their titles name the islands, capes, bays, winds, ocean currents, seasons, gems, exotic spices and sea creatures – the course of the voyage and the spoils. Yet this apparently Stevensonian adventure story turns out to have more in common with Golding's *Lord of the Flies:*

A trip up river? Once I asked
this question, but dawn banged its burnt eyelid shut
and I forgot, I died…

Under my eyelids
a war of colours, pulsating departure point for blood.

Blood, life-giving and life-taking, becomes an important image in *Colonies*. Our bodies become the fourth element besides fire, water and air; our skin, the territory of transgression, the boundary to be crossed. But that's what experience is all about. It can be scored by the scars – they will prove to us that we are not phantoms, after all; that we are not fakes, as if the originals have fallen asleep and 'died a little'. What is more, death will now have a problem: 'the dead one' will be difficult to recognise 'in the interior of the ocean, in the drop of hard blood'. Blood entices the word, this 'huge and wild child' which 'with its black tongue will have to taste somebody's blood every night.'

Różycki (b. 1970) knows the power and voracity of the word. Nine poems, interwoven into this survey of colonies, contemplate the possible outcomes of his encounters with words – they all start with the same line: 'when I began to write, I didn't know yet,' to be followed by an ironic list of afflictions and benefits. In two poems with maps in their titles – 'Fake Maps' and 'Burnt Maps' – words, language, tongue can be used to check the fate of those who have fallen asleep, those who have hidden under the ground, 'more deeply than generations of ants'.

Such a linguistic probing, a test with one's own tongue, was performed in the Ukraine, in the former Polish borderland. Różycki lives in Opole, territory that once belonged to Germans, but after the Second World War became part of Poland and the home of Poles deported from the eastern borderlands. The 'hiding' of relatives in 'Burnt Maps' suggests absences caused not only by death. Therefore the speaker has to lie down with his face on the ground and talk to it, feel their presence in 'the huge, wild grass' growing round his head. Not by chance is the grass described by the same two adjectives that name the attributes of the word.

Not by chance do the words of these four poets await the verdict of the 'Nike' jury.

Ian McDonough

Sky Above Bank of Scotland, Forfar

Beneath the surface hum and haw of High Street
lies a bubbling guilty brew,
a heady soup of secrets
coursing through the shoppers' veins –
dishwater thin,
salty as the blood of slaughtered kine.

Sun or rain, it's all the same to Jocky Black:
he's had a snifter, doesna care who kens it.
Scything through the pavement gossip,
booted up and armour-clad in filthy tweed,
he halts to check his pockets.

Outside the bank Jock counts warm notes,
pausing to cast a scowl
at clouds that race like ferrets
through the dirty sky.
Trousering his wad, he strikes for home
to spoon black earth into a floral bowl
and fill his gut with substance.

Sky Above Premier Travel Inn, Aberdeen South

Beached here, seven miles from the sea,
with ten Silk Cut and an undistinguished Chianti,
I'm looking to the skies for help.

Last night I conjured up my father
administering pints in the Bayview Hotel –
fag in mouth, wings, halo above his head.

He served me some advice – 'Steady boy,
keep scanning the horizon for a sail.'
But the digital TV is glutted with atrocities,

and all the view reflects is my flat memory,
the simple history of an estuary
where fresh meets salt but is too cool to mingle.

Choking in this comfort with no comfort near at hand
I feel like some confused, pathetic Moses
peering through the fence that guards the Promised Land.

Sky Above Supermarket Car Park, Dalkeith

Autumn is rolling down the Summer aisles
winking at brassica
cold-shouldering the happy sugar biscuits
basking in a background radiation glow.
Chickens, shiny, fat as hatchbacks,
grow incontinent with pumped-up love.

Seasonal terrors snuggle down like snakes
among dried figs, the potted heads
the goose-down flesh. Earth's crust
is banished to Home Baking,
shelved along with fructose, pectin, yeast,
dwarfed among the spray-on megafoods.

And Autumn, fingering the household shelves,
has found a brand of cleaning agent
that will wipe your mind for half the price.
Grey matter seeps
from underneath each frozen food compartment door.
The Manager cannot stem the tide,
his shoppers watch in anxious ecstacy
as flat-screen clouds build over Elsinore.

Outside a watery spring vegetable light
glances off the credit cards
held heavenward to snare its golden rays.

Sky Above Premier Travel Inn, Inverness

Some ancient Celtic water god
is emptying the contents of his stomach
over the streets of this rural city.

I'm peering upwards hopefully
as an all-absorbing blackness
pinpoints the vacuum in his eyes.

Have mercy on us, water god,
we who roam from Travelodge to Travel Inn,
chasing fleeting smiles from strangers.

After the rain, high grey wisps pattern the dark
like flecks from the water god's foaming maw.

I slip the outside world beneath my bed.

Morning reassembles me, glues back together
all the flimsy furniture that sleep has trashed.

Laura Solomon

The Killing Jar

My son collects insects. The idea was planted in his mind when I took him to the Museum of Natural History and he saw how even the tiniest of creatures, with the most meagre of life spans, could have a chance to live forever. He stood thoughtfully before a cabinet that contained numerous prime specimens, all neatly labelled with both the Latin and the common names.

'They were killed by somebody a long time ago,' he said. 'And now they will never die. Isn't that right, Dad?'

'Yes Gerald, that's right.'

I was listening with only half an ear. My mind was elsewhere. Relations between his mother and me had been a little fraught and I was thinking how best to protect him from our storms. I wanted to keep him safe. I wanted him to be happy. He tugged at my sleeve.

'Can I start a collection, Dad? Can I, please? Just a small one.'

'Sure you can. I'll help. Come on, let's go get an ice cream. I saw a Mr Whippy van parked up outside.'

The Emperor of Ice Cream, lurking on every other street corner. I bought him a cone full of soft white mush, took his hand, led him away from the museum. I'd thought that would be the end of the insect talk, but it turned out to be only the beginning.

*

Eleanor and I provided encouragement; we thought a hobby would be good for him. We let him use the garden shed as his workroom. For his tenth birthday I bought him a copy of Murray S. Upton's *Methods for Collecting, Preserving and Studying Insects and Allied Forms.* He memorised entire passages. I helped him prepare his tools of the trade; gave him a hand with the killing jar, the relaxing chamber, the spreading board. The killing jar was simple, just a basic preserving jar, into which we placed two inches of sawdust, before pouring over Plaster of Paris and allowing the mix to set, thereby creating an absorbent layer that was regularly soaked with nail polish remover. The little critters were knocked out instantly, humanely. The relaxing chamber, which prevented the insects from becoming too dry and brittle, was a plastic box in which sat a layer of sand that was moistened with water and rubbing alcohol. Across the top was a sheet of cardboard upon which you would place the insects that were in need of relaxation.

'Yeah, chill out dudes,' said Gerald, as he placed his first victims, a couple of lacewing moths and a small spider into his chamber.

The spreading board was knocked together from balsa wood and glue. Good easy fun. Clean.

He wasn't fussy; any insect was a good insect to him. Shortly after he'd taken up his new hobby I overheard Eleanor on the phone to one of her friends.

'Oh yes,' she was saying. 'He'd pin and mount anything. Yes, he *does* take after his father.'

Cockroaches, beetles, wasps, bees, grasshoppers, crickets, stick insects, butterflies, angel insects. The odd praying mantis. What had begun as a hobby had blossomed into an obsession. Nothing went to waste. The larger insects he pinned to cotton wool-coated cardboard before putting them in a frame. Some of his works he gave away to startled friends and relatives, some he kept for himself. The smaller insects, or those otherwise unsuitable for pinning, were placed into a specimen cabinet that we picked up cheap from a garage sale. He was a neurotic labeller; nothing went unclassified. He'd learnt that at the museum, the importance of naming.

At first he was clumsy; there were numerous torn wings and split thoraxes, but within just a few weeks he'd mastered his art. He was swift, deft, deadly. From field to preserved state took less than twenty-four hours. One second you'd be happily flitting amongst the long grass, enjoying the warmth of the sun on your wings, the next you'd be snuffing it in his jar. His speciality was butterflies. To him there was no greater thrill than slamming his net down over those fluttering wings, capturing what had once been free. He was in love with the object; I was in love with the word. Entomology was his passion; etymology was mine.

I already knew a little about the word's origin, enough to know that nobody knows for certain where it comes from, though it's commonly assumed to stem from the notion that butterflies, or witches in that form, stole butter and milk. Online, I gleaned further random facts. The Greek word for butterfly was psyche, originally meaning 'soul' or 'breath', now meaning 'mind'. Is that what Gerald was catching, tiny minds? The Maori believe that the soul of a dead person comes back to the world as a butterfly. Was that what my son was framing on the wall - the souls of the dead?

It was after midnight when I took the call. The phone's ring awoke my wife, who switched on the table lamp, sat upright in bed and eyed me, hawk-like, as I spoke into the receiver. Even before she spoke, I knew who it was. Who else would call at that time of night?

'Hello.'

'You promised me this wouldn't happen again. I was waiting for over an hour.'

'Oh dear. Yes. Oh yes, I am sorry. That's terrible news.'

'What?'

'I'm terribly sorry to hear that. Please, if there's anything I can do…'

'Yeah, there's something you can do. You can stay the hell away from me. It's over, Lawrence. Goodbye.'

Click.

'Well?'

My wife raised an eyebrow.

'That was my cousin,' I lied. 'Her mother passed away last night.'

'Cousin schmousin.'

'You don't believe a word I say, do you?'

'I gave up believing years ago, Larry. I just wish you'd stop insulting me by spinning so much bullshit. A web of shit. That's what you've spun.'

What was I supposed to say to that?

'Night then, dear. Sweet dreams.'

Her reply was another *click,* the switching off of the light. I wasn't too worried by the phone call. My wife already knew what was going on – it was no great revelation to her.

'We stay together for Gerald,' was what she told other people, though she must also have had her own private reasons for not leaving.

As for the other one, well, I knew from experience that she didn't mean a word she said. It had been over five times before.

Gerald's favourite place was the field behind our house; to him it was Elysian, paradisiacal. It was where he went to escape from Eleanor and me when we started arguing. Sometimes he returned with Tupperware containers full of creatures, sometimes he simply lay and watched his insect friends buzzing and feeding and mating, returned home empty-handed, having chosen to capture nothing.

It was late and we were in the middle of a blazing row when he found it. I don't recall now what we were arguing about, but we stopped short when he entered the house with a dark, scuttling shape in a clear plastic container.

'I've found something new,' he said.

He was excited, a puppy with a fresh bone, salivating almost.

'Gerald!' exclaimed Eleanor. 'I thought you were up in your room. What were you doing in the field at this time of night? It's freezing out there. You'll catch your death.'

She held her hands to his cheeks.

'You need a hot shower,' she said. 'You need to warm up.'

Gerald was too jubilant to feel the cold.

'Look,' he said.

He peeled the lid of the Tupperware back a centimetre or so and we peered inside. It seemed nothing remarkable, an ordinary spider, just like all the other spiders he'd brought home. But to Gerald it was extraordinary, a miracle.

'I'll bet you anything you like,' he said. 'that nobody else has ever captured one quite like this.'

At first we refused to believe him. It seemed impossible that something undiscovered could exist so close to home. We looked through all the literature, the many books on arachnids he'd withdrawn from the library, and searched extensively on that other web, the one spun in cyberspace. This exact spider was to be found nowhere, though we stumbled across photos of a few of its cousins.

'Looks like a wolf spider to me,' Gerald said, with the air of an expert. 'Lycosidae family.'

Thwack.

With one swift swipe of a book he swatted dead a fly that was buzzing against the windowpane, and dropped it into the spider's lair. The spider stalked, leapt, snacked.

'See how it pounces on its prey. It doesn't need a web to hunt. But look at those faint yellow markings. It's new, Dad. A new guy. You know what this means! I get to name it.'

I indulged him. If he was wrong, the world's biologists would soon put him to rights. *Pardosa geraldus* – the moniker he chose. PG for short. We published our findings in *BMC Evolutionary Biology*. Nobody protested, nobody said, 'I got here before you. This is not new.' It was official. The unknown had become known.

PG was placed in a special ice cream container that Gerald painted blue so that nobody would mistake it for garbage. We sliced holes in the lid. The container sat on top of the television, a sunny spot, a place for basking. Gerald joked that the spider seemed to improve our reception, especially when we turned to Channel Four, which was notoriously static-prone in our part of London. Sticks and leaves were provided by way of habitat; he was fed bugs that were captured especially for him. Sometimes I fancied that I could hear PG shuffling about in his container at night, munching on sandflies, blades of grass stabbing at his body and legs, like tiny green blades. But that was only my imagination, a flight of fancy. Even a man with the hearing of a wolf would have been unable to hear such sounds, from where he lay, upstairs in his bed beside a wife full of muted fury.

A week later she called me at the university.

'Well?' she said.

Not even so much as a preliminary 'hello'.

'Well what?'

'Well what do you have to say for yourself?'

'Not a lot.'

'Let me ask you this. Why did you even bother to arrange to meet if you weren't going to show up? Was it some kind of game? Yet another pathetic attempt to try and gain the upper hand? To assert your feeble manhood?'

'I forgot. It was Gerald's birthday.'

'Don't *lie* to me.'

'I have to go now.'

'Yes, that's right. Run back to your words and their origins. You're doing the world such a big fucking service. That's *just* what the masses are crying out for; another tome from Lawrence E. Hopkins.'

'I have to give a lecture.'

'Well don't keep your loyal following waiting.'

Click.

I know what I am to her - I am shades of grey, shifting sands. Unreliable. Treacherous. The truth is that if I left Eleanor to be with her she wouldn't want me; I would become boring, predictable, dull, soon to be discarded like last year's handbag. It's only because I am unattainable that she wants to attain me. From a distance, I glitter. Up close, I am muted, matt. I open up the gap between us and she falls right into it. Time and again, she falls right in. I extend a hand only to snatch it away when she reaches out to grasp it. She thinks I will fill some hole, some inner emptiness, but I only tear it open wider. To my wife, I am something different. To Eleanor I am rigid, stubborn.

'Everything's black and white to you, isn't it?' she asked once, rhetorically. What she meant was that I am inflexible, narrow-minded, but I chose to take it as a compliment. Blackness absorbs everything. White light contains all colours.

After the lecture, I called her back and arranged to meet her that Sunday, in order to explain. You have to keep extending a bit of hope, or they get up and walk away from the chessboard. Hard to play against an absent opponent. She likes art galleries; I took her to the Tate Modern. She wore black, like a mourner at a funeral; a black pencil skirt, a black turtleneck, dark sunglasses that she kept on, even inside, where we looked at Cindy Sherman's self portraits and rooms full of plain white boxes. Her red hair was slicked back in a neat bun. I held her hand, moved my thumb back and forth, as if to reassure her.

'I know it seems impossible,' I said. 'But please, hold on. I just need to wait until Gerald is old enough to leave home and then I'll leave too. I promise.'

'I know your promises. I've heard it all before, Lawrence.'

'If you won't wait for me, why should I continue to see you?'

That's it, turn it around, throw it back onto her. She sniffed haughtily, but she didn't let go of my hand, even after we'd left the gallery and were wandering slowly towards the hotel.

I was in my study researching the origins of the word 'arachnid' when he knocked at my door. He entered before I could answer, came creeping in on cat feet, stood at my elbow.

'What's up, love?'

'It's PG, Dad. He seems angry.'

'Angry? What does an angry spider look like?'

'He's pawing at the bottom of his container. Like this.'

With his right arm he mimed a pawing action and he snorted a little through his nose, like a bull about to charge.

'Oh dear. I see. And what do you think he's angry about?'

'He told me something.'

'He *told* you something. Goodness. I didn't realise that you spoke spiderese.'

'We have our own special language. Halfway between spiderese and human.'

'Ah. You've reached a compromise. So what did he say?'

'Where were you today, Dad?'

'Today? I just went out for a bit. To meet a friend from university. You want Dad to have friends, don't you?'

'Yeah, but…'

'But what?'

'Nothing.'

'So, come on then. What did PG say?'

'He said that you had another girlfriend. Besides Mum. A different one.'

'Now where would he have heard a silly thing like that?'

'He overheard Mum talking on the phone.'

'Well, he must have misheard then, Trucker Boy, because Daddy only has one lady and that's your mother. Just one. There are no others.'

'Stop calling me Trucker Boy, I hate that name.'

'Okay then *Gerald*, he must have misheard.'

'PG said that Mum said that you might leave us.'

'Relax. I'm not going anywhere. Where would I go?'

I held out my cheek for a kiss and he gave it a small, suspicious peck. He did not turn and walk away; instead he backed out the door. I could feel his eyes boring into me as I crouched over my computer, pretending to return to my work.

Three days later, further signs of trouble. White static on the TV screen; terrible reception. Rising from the sofa to tweak the antennae, I noticed that the lid of PG's container had been changed. An unpunctured black cover now kept him captive. How could he live through that? All God's creatures need oxygen. Gerald was upstairs in his room, playing Gran Turismo. I could hear the revving of computerised engines, the screech of digital tyres. I climbed the stairs, entered the room, stood right behind him. He didn't look round, just sat there with his eyes on the screen, making *vroom-vroom* noises as his body swung left and right with the movement of his car.

'Gerald! Did you change PG's lid?'

'Yeah. He was getting bored of the old one.'

'But there're no holes in it, Gerald. How's he supposed to breathe?'

'Oh yeah, I forgot. Sorry.'

He took a turn too fast, lost control, went skidding into a wall.

'Fuck!'

'Please don't swear in this house. Now where's his old lid? Let's put that one back on.'

'I threw it in the bin.'

'Gerald, honestly. Sometimes you just don't think.'

'Yeah, whatever.'

'If you can't take care of PG properly, he'll have to go back to the field.'

'Oh, high score!!'

A number flashed on the screen. He entered his name in the Hall of Fame, hit Play, started a new game. I closed the door on my son and returned to the living room, where I removed PG's black lid and gave him a new, clear one, with sufficient slices in it. Then I went into my study to make a call.

*

I took her to the park. She likes parks. It was close to home, dangerous, I liked that. Had you climbed up onto the roof of our house you could have seen us, walking past the duck pond, which was beginning to ice over. Winter was drawing in. Most of the ducks had flown elsewhere, just a few hardy stragglers remained, huddled together, as if for warmth.

'So here we are again, then,' she said. 'The same old pattern. Going nowhere fast.'

'It's only a question of time,' I replied.

'You're a stuck record.'

'More like looptape, I think. Still, something's better than nothing, isn't it?'

She smiled a little, though it could have been a grimace. My right hand gripped her left elbow. I led her in amongst a small copse of trees. Pulled her down into the dirt.

Eleanor was at yoga. She liked to stay supple, flexible. Sometimes I wondered if she wasn't having an affair herself – why else would she care so much about keeping in shape? It's not as if it was for my benefit. Gerald and I were sitting on the sofa watching *Big Brother*; fame decoupled from achievement.

'Spoke to PG again today, Dad.'

'Really? What did he say? I suppose he was angry with you for trying to suffocate him.'

'Na, he's forgotten all about that. He told me something else.'

'And what was that? What did the spider say?'

Any day now, I would tire of this game.

'He said he saw you in the park. Holding hands with a woman that wasn't Mum. A lady with red hair.'

'Now how would he have seen that from his home? Can he see through walls?'

'He got bored and crawled out through one of the holes. Pulled it open with one leg. Went out for a bit of wander.'

'Is that so?'

'He's got a lot of eyes, Dad. He sees things.'

'So it would seem.'

'He said you were having it off in the bushes.'

'*Having it off*? Where did you learn that terrible expression?'

'From PG.'

'Ah.'

'I'm not saying it's true, Dad. I'm just repeating what I heard.'

'Spoken like a true gossip. Listen, can two people play that Gran Turismo?'

'Yeah. If they want.'

'Come on then. I'll challenge you to a duel.'

I put one arm around his shoulders and we headed up to his room where I let him beat me by a couple of laps.

Sunday morning. Eleanor busying herself in the kitchen. She liked us to breakfast as a family at the weekend – a semblance of togetherness. A hollow imitation of family life. Stepping out to fetch the newspaper; broken eggshells on the front doorstep, egg all down the door. My Ford Mondeo had also been targeted. I'd thought such petty, spiteful acts of vengeance were beneath her, but clearly I was mistaken. She'd always behaved with a certain level of dignity, but now the mask was slipping, the cracks were beginning to appear. Perhaps I was jumping to conclusions. It could have been somebody else. Neighbourhood kids skylarking about. Returning with a copy of *The Guardian*, I found Eleanor with the fridge door open.

'Where have all the eggs gone?' she asked. 'Who's eaten all the eggs? I bought a fresh dozen just yesterday.'

'Not me,' I said.

'Gerald,' she yelled up the stairs. 'Gerald, have you been into the eggs?'

'No, Mum.'

The distant drone of Gran Turismo, the soundtrack to our lives.

'I wish he'd quit playing that bloody game,' said Eleanor. 'Damn, I'll have to go to the shop. Make Gerald take a shower and come down and join us, would you?'

She put on some lipstick and collected her handbag from the sofa. I took a bucket and a sponge and cleaned up the mess.

A table for two at her favourite restaurant. She let me order for her, she's not good at making decisions, at least, not when she's with me. In her other life, her *real* life, she works as a lawyer in the city, a forceful, determined woman with a mind of her own. What I see is the other side, what she hides from those city boys, from her clients, from her small circle of friends. I am time out, time apart. A poisonous chink in her armour. Before the entrées arrived, I handed her the gift I'd bought to keep her happy, a single diamond, set in white gold, dangling from a thin chain. She gasped when she saw it, withdrew it from the box. It dangled from her fingers, sparkling in the light like a dangerous star.

'Oh, it's beautiful,' she said.

'It suits you. Here, let me help you put it on.'

I rose from my chair, stood behind her, draped the chain around her neck, fastened the clasp. Then I bent down low and whispered, 'I just can't give you up.'

Even to my own ears, the words sounded rehearsed, clichéd, corny. She smiled with one side of her mouth.

That night I didn't go home at all; instead I stayed with her, in her austere apartment. It hadn't happened before.

'It won't happen again,' I said to Eleanor when I returned at midday.

She stared at me icily.

'Go and look in the kitchen,' she said.

On the table there was a pleasant surprise. *Pardosa geraldus*, dead in the killing jar, brought inside as gory evidence, as a cat would leave the gift of a slain mouse for its owner.

'Ever so *Fatal Attraction*,' said Eleanor. 'If you're going to fuck somebody, at least chose someone who won't come creeping round the house, murdering my son's pets. Well, goodbye PG.'

She upended the jar and the spider slid into the bin.

'Where's Gerald?'

'Where do you think?'

In his usual place, hunched over the Playstation controls like a boy possessed.

'Gerald, did you know that PG was dead?'

'Course. I found him this morning. Out in the work shed.'

'Why did you kill him? I thought you were proud of your discovery.'

'I didn't kill him! He crept in there all by himself.'

'Do you mean to tell me that he somehow escaped from his ice cream container, crawled all the way from the house to the shed and committed suicide?'

'I guess.'

'Why would he go and do a thing like that?'

'He wasn't happy.'

'Why wasn't he happy? He had a nice home and plenty to eat.'

'I dunno, Dad. Spiders aren't logical. Score. High*est* score!'

'Some people have to win, don't they?' said Eleanor.

She'd followed me up the stairs and had been listening at the door.

'Yes,' I said. 'Some people do.'

It was only later, when challenging my son to another game of Gran Turismo, that I noticed that each time he won it was himself he was beating, for his was the only name that featured in that particular Hall of Fame.

Elżbieta Wiącek

The 'Polish Film School'
Its Genesis and Development

translated by David Malcolm

Before the Second World War dozens of films were produced annually in Poland. They were not, however, distinguished in terms of quality. Polish cinema was unable to shape its own aesthetic, but drew inspiration largely from cosmopolitan models. Cinematography was dominated by private producers who preferred commercial, highly conventionalised, narrative models.

After 1945, by a miraculous set of circumstances, people of a variety of political backgrounds joined efforts to resuscitate the national film industry and organise it on new principles. While supporting the development of an art cinema, at the same time they wished it to be a collective cinema – each film unit was run by an experienced director under whose eye debut directors worked.

This new cinema's first successes were Wanda Jakubowska's *Ostatni etap* (The Last Stage, 1948) and Aleksander Ford's *Ulica Graniczna* (Border Street, 1949). Jakubowska, who had been in a German concentration camp, made the first non-documentary film in the world about the mass murder organised by the Nazis. Ford concentrated on the Holocaust. The culminating sequence in his film is the Jewish Ghetto Uprising. The universal humanism of these images was not appreciated by the Party authorities. Paradoxically, the authorities feared the success of Polish films because then – in their view – the makers of such films would slip out of their control. Despite everything, sovietisation was not very intense up to 1948. The propaganda function of the cinema was not yet an absolute requirement. However, a year later, at the convention of Polish filmmakers, socialist realism was declared the only acceptable path to follow, limiting the depiction of reality to that of class conflict. Films that faithfully followed Soviet models predominated. They were centred on schematic and unambiguous characters.

In 1948 in Łódź, the first Polish Film Academy was opened. From its very beginning it was the site of two wholly different visions. The authorities saw in it a forge for producing ideologically sound cadres. The graduates' task was to fix the principles of communism and the leading role of the Soviet Union in the consciousness of Polish society. The teachers, however, had no intention of isolating the students; on the contrary, for them the cinema was a world art form. Thus, the students were taught using examples from the French avant garde of the 1920s (René Clair, Luis Buñuel) and German Expressionism. Watching these films, young filmmakers became convinced that formally experimental art cinema had already achieved a great deal. They realised that they had to find a new path and look for it in *what* a film tells of, and not only *how*. For the same reason Andrzej Wajda, after two years of studies at the Art Academy, gave up painting in the manner of Paul Cézanne, because he felt that this was not part of his world. Years later the director wrote in his autobiography of his decision: 'We had seen the War from close up. We had experienced injustice. Can a still life depicting a bowl of cherries express that?… I understood that our generation must relate the fate of our fathers, for the dead can no longer speak.' The need to reread recent history was strengthened by the fact that hitherto (apart from works dedicated to the martyrology of the concentration camps) the theme of the war had been avoided in Polish culture, or presented inaccurately.

For this whole generation, the most important theme was the experience of the Second World War. Artists rejected the conventions of pre-war Polish cinema (often it combined sections of dialogue with songs). They felt a greater affinity with the traditions of neorealism, because that is how they saw themselves. The films which mark the beginning of the 'Polish school of film making,' Andrzej Wajda's debut film *Pokolenie* (Generation, 1954) and Jerzy Kawalerowicz's *Celuloza* (Cellulose, 1954), allude to the tradition of neorealism through *mise-en-scène*, photography, outdoor settings, and by bringing new actors onto the screen.

In the mid-1950s, during the ideological 'thaw' of that time, new and bolder creative possibilities opened up for cinematography. In 1955 film companies were created that were to some degree independent creative units. Thanks to this, filmmakers gained a certain amount of influence over the choice of topics for their films. It was an embodiment of the idea of independence in artistic and production matters.

In 1956 three important films came to the screen: Andrzej Wajda's *Kanał* (Sewer), Andrzej Munk's *Człowiek na torze* (Man on the Track) and Tadeusz Konwicki's *Ostatni dzień lata* (The Last Day of Summer). This last film anticipates the achievements of the French *nouvelle vague* in the way it was made (the film was created by a group of several close friends). Konwicki (also, it should be noted, a writer of fiction) was further a precursor in terms of theme: the plot is limited to the meeting on a beach of a man and a woman who share the fate of their lost generation, people damaged by the war. Despite the fact that both long for a close relationship with another person, their traumatic experiences make it impossible for them to begin a stable relationship.

The concept of the 'Polish school', which had been rather timidly advanced up to now in Poland itself, appeared in reviews and foreign publicity materials along with a Silver Palm for *Kanał* at the International Film Festival in Cannes. The fact that this film was presented abroad reveals an amazing confidence on the part of the communist authorities, all the more so because Wajda's debut had been harshly criticised as a portrait of the lumpenproletariat, quite without any Marxist consciousness. *Kanał* owes its authenticity to Jerzy Stefan Stawiński's screenplay, in which he describes his own experiences from the Warsaw Uprising of 1944. The film, which depicts a fatal attempt to escape through Warsaw's sewers by Polish insurgents, questions the sense of the Uprising in which almost the entire young intelligentsia of Warsaw died (200,000 of the city's inhabitants lost their lives in total). Wajda's choice of a looser form of narrative permitted a diverse depiction of characters' psychologies and allowed him to analyse the mechanics of destruction. Wajda inverts the usual meanings connected with the symbolism of light and dark. The darkness underground means safety, while space filled with sunlight means the presence of the enemy and the threat of physical annihilation.

The Western press interpreted *Kanał* in the spirit of the Existentialists' notion of human fate. The French critic Ado Kyrou writes forcefully in *Positif* (1957): 'Wajda is the only young European filmmaker in this time of intellectual laziness who achieves a powerful, passionate voice that recalls Buñuel.' For the makers of the film, the American reaction was the most surprising; American commentators were impressed by the scriptwriter's imagination – they did not believe that such events really took place. In Poland *Kanał* unleashed a wave of polemics: instead of a proud monument, the makers of *Kanał* had shown the nightmare of defeat and psychologically shattered fighters whose heroism had been in vain. Critic Juliusz Kydryński, in 'Surrealism?,' *Życie literackie*, 1957, questioned this picture of the heroism of the Uprising drowned in excrement. But *Kanał* is not anti-heroic; it is just anti-bombastic; sometimes the director himself falls for heroism's desperate fascination. Wajda would only take up an orthodox position towards unreflective heroism in *Lotna* (Lotna, 1959) – a film showing the reality of September 1939. The famous scene of this vision is the Polish cavalry's charge with drawn sabres against German tanks.

Giving a historical topic a contemporary dimension is also a feature of Wajda's next film, *Popiół i diament* (Ashes and Diamonds, 1958). This adaptation of Jerzy Andrzejewski's novel diverges considerably from the original. The protagonist is not the communist activist but the insurgent full of ethical dilemmas, torn between a desire for a normal life and love, on one hand, and obligation towards his right-wing rebel group, on the other. This tragic figure was played by Zbigniew Cybulski, an actor who became an idol for young people in the late 1950s. He was convinced that only a complete biological union with a given role could create a living person on screen. In every role he played, Cybulski invariably maintained his trademark image, wearing the dark glasses which became for him something like the mask worn by actors in the classical theatre. His masked face (it is the eyes that communicate most vividly with an audience) had to have some equivalent; this was his physical outline, which conveyed feelings with unusual clarity. It was this that brought him close to the style of the New York Actors' Studio. Polish and foreign critics called him the 'Polish James Dean'. The tragic paradox of history – declares *Popiół i diament* – is that both the victim and the assassin, representing quite different ideological stances, are the best of all the characters shown on screen.

The Polish school of filmmaking was hugely varied. The voice of Andrzej Munk (1921–61), that of a cool rationalist, is marked by irony and even a certain degree of maliciousness that unmasks national faults. His first film, *Człowiek na torze* (Man on the Track, 1956) refers in a straightforward and serious way to the experiences of Stalinism, not via political events, but through the tragic influence of the epoch on an individual fate. Just like Orson Welles's eponymous hero in *Citizen Kane*, the protagonist of *Człowiek na torze* remains an empty space which one must fill out; others' views of him cannot explain everything. Munk is interested in the birth and development of myth. As Eberhardt Konrad remarks in *O polskich filmach* (Warsaw, 1982) he may have been a rationalist, but he knew that the truth of material reality borders on the 'non-truth' of the world of the human mind. For his personal screen polemic with *Kanał,* Munk wickedly chose the title of the emotional Third Symphony (*The Eroica*) by Beethoven. In the first part of *Eroika* (*The Eroica*, 1957), a certain Mr Górkiewicz (played by Edward Dziewoński) is accidentally caught up in the events of the Warsaw Uprising. He approaches his countrymen's struggle with scepticism and prefers to escape from the burning city. By chance, however, he is charged with a mission that may determine the fate of the capital. In contrast to the expressionist inflection of Wajda's film, here the grotesque is dominant. In the second part, the Poles are simultaneously ridiculous and tragic. In a closely guarded prisoner-of-war camp, there is born a myth that the inmates need: the legend of a successful escape by one of them. The truth turns out to be brutal – their hero is dying hidden in an attic, and in the end he commits suicide. The exploded myth, however, does not change into sneering. The film suggests that for bankrupt people, smashed up by history, myth is absolutely necessary. But the author's intentions were not understood in Poland. The aura of sanctity which surrounded the national armed struggle meant that Munk was accused of lampooning Poland. The outraged director defended himself thus: '*The Eroica* says nothing bad about heroes, moreover the representatives of those irrational positions are shown with sympathy. We just point to the uselessness of that type of demonstration.'

Zezowate szczęście (Cross-Eyed Happiness, 1959) broadens the field of historical discussion – backwards to the interwar period and forwards to the times of Stalinism. The film showed that the average man, represented by the cowardly hero Piszczyk, was not able to meet Polish ambitious standards of personal conduct. Playing the role of Piszczyk, Bogumił Kobiela created a portrait of the eternal conformist, a perfect embodiment of Erich Fromm's model of 'the escape from freedom.' *Zezowate szczęście* implicates everyone – the hero and the audience that sympathises with him. Individual sections of the film are done in the manner of comedies from the appropriate period. This gives the effect of postmodern collage: Charlie Chaplin interweaves with René Clair, and Jacques Tati with Frank Capra.

Robert Bresson thought *Zezowate szczęście* the best Polish film. In his opinion it is the one film in the history of world cinema that shows so accurately the phenomenon of the liveliness of mediocrity. Bresson was struck by the fact that Piszczyk combines in himself passivity and weakness with indestructability and huge vitality. He constantly changes clothes, trying to choose the appropriate uniform according to circumstances. History, however, demands to be treated seriously and constantly punishes the conformist.

When, at the start of the 1960s, the main current of the 'Polish school' began to show signs of decline, voices began to be heard pointing to the philosophical superficiality of the school and to the absence of a universal dimension in its products. An answer to such criticism came from Jerzy Kawalerowicz. *Matka Joanna od aniołów* (Mother Joanna of the Angels, 1961), based on Jarosław Iwaszkiewicz's short story, referred to a celebrated occurrence in seventeenth-century France. The story of the possession of the head of a convent in Loudun was transferred to eighteenth-century Poland. It is a film about human nature and human nature's defence against restrictions imposed from without. It is the story of the love of a man and a woman who belong to religious orders. For the nun and the exorcist, love and faith remain in conflict, which leads to fanaticism and crime. *Matka Joanna od aniołów* represented Poland at Cannes and won a Silver Palm. Captivated by the film's visual composition, the French critic Georges Sadoul pointed to its references to paintings by Georges de la Tour and Caravaggio. Polish criticism praised the universal humanism of the work, although the Catholic press accused it of being anti-religious. Generally, the film was not associated with the 'Polish school,' but it is possible to see it as related to that movement: it shows the same revolt against dogmas; it has the same vision of the futility of sacrifice.

Parallel with Kawalerowicz, Andrzej Munk undertook something similar

Pasażerka (The Passenger), made in 1961 and not completed because of the director's tragic death. The film brought together two stories: the experiences of a German female concentration camp guard and her current reflections about one of the women prisoners. Munk was interested by the dialectic and morally unsettling relation of executioner and victim. In an unusually powerful way the film showed a culture and its humanist values in crisis. It extended the borders of the Polish cinema in terms of world filmmaking.

In the polyphony of the 'Polish school of filmmaking', the work of Jerzy Has has a particular position. He is often called an 'individual artist' and a 'poet of time', and his films are described as 'memory's lumber room'. Has is convinced that art depends on subjectivity and creates its own worlds. Almost always, his point of departure is imagination, literature and the operation of time. He stresses how complex time's material is. In *Jak być kochaną* (How to Be Loved, 1963) time is the final judge, fixing the value of victims. The heroine (played by Barbara Krafft) hides the man she loves (Zbigniew Cybulski). The woman takes a risk, suffers humiliation (she is raped by the Gestapo), but in the end she is unable to save him from committing suicide. The film simultaneously accepts the conventions of the 'Polish school' and offers an unusually bitter moral: all human efforts turn out to be in vain. The film is based on retrospects. We see the heroine in two time settings: in her present distance towards the world, and in her past naive belief in the sense of sacrifice. In Wajda's films the War is a still relevant catastrophe, demanding judgments; in Has's film it is an image dulled by the distance of time, and time is the 'positive hero' that permits one to mature internally.

Making his debut within the framework of the 'Polish school,' Kazimierz Kutz (b. 1929) chooses a more modest focus, showing Polish concerns through the prism of individuals' fates. From the beginning he was aware of the path he had taken: 'analysing what Munk and Wajda had done, it seemed to me that they always tell about the subject rather than the human being, which in any case is, in my view, one of the basic failings of our national art. Too often it aims for grand effects, losing in that way what is most essential: the necessity of speaking about great matters through the fate of the individual.' While the majority of directors drew on a pre-war upper-class tradition, Kutz turned towards a more popular/proletarian one. His *Krzyż walecznych* (Cross of the Brave, 1959) was the first account within the 'Polish school' of peasant soldiers. The film showed their encounter with the devastated country and their complex relation to the enemy. The heroes' encounter with a Nazi dog, which they cannot bring themselves to kill, is particularly engaging. Kutz also shows the 'cult of memory' taken to an absurd level. When the war hero's beautiful widow starts to meet with another man, she exposes herself to the outrage of the whole small town in which she lives.

In the visually original *Nikt nie woła* (No One Cries Out, 1960), Kutz enters into a dialogue with Wajda's *Popiół i diament* (Ashes and Diamonds). Its protagonist – a negative reflection of Wajda's hero – refuses to commit a murder. This breaks with the fatalism of the 'Polish school,' with the unavoidable deaths of its protagonists. In *Ktokolwiek wie...* (Whoever Knows..., 1966), Kutz succeeded in devaluing plot. There did remain some sort of skeleton of exciting action, but, a little like in Antonioni's films, only to discount completely its dramaturgical necessity. The film's reality is unknown and mysterious, that of the Polish suburbs. Its inhabitants are uprooted from their places and communities; they have lost social bonds and live in isolation, in deepening loneliness. We learn very little about them: the director limits himself to what he sees and hears, not filling in the empty spaces with seeming knowledge. What is best in Kutz's films lies not in the plot, but in his sincere gaze at another human being.

Kutz is not just the representative of a plebeian current in Polish cinema. He created a thematic enclave, drawing on the country of his childhood – Silesia, the mining region in the south of Poland. *Sól ziemi czarnej* (Salt of the Black Earth, 1970) and *Perła w koronie* (Pearl in the Crown, 1972) tell of this – for the director – mythic land. In form they recall the pictures of naïve painters.

The representatives of the 'Polish school' created a *directors' cinema*. Each one of its directors was an artistic individual, but they were linked by a feeling of community. To a great degree the school of Polish film owes its high level to a fruitful encounter with literature. The basis of the majority of their films was literary works written with a huge sense of authorial responsibility and which dealt with contemporary topics.

Film in the People's Republic of Poland emerged and was distributed exclusively within the framework of a state monopoly. State control was its basis: the source of film tape was thoroughly controlled. Permission for a film to be made was not final. If the preliminary project was accepted, the screenplay could be written. This was then reviewed by a special commission made up of Party officials and filmmakers. Thus, in order to avoid restrictions, directors expressed their attitude to post-war reality mainly through *image*. 'It is easy to censor words because ideology is contained in words,' Wajda has observed. 'However for an image there are at least two points of view. Let's take, for example, the ending of *Popiół i diament* – the death of the hero on a rubbish tip. The censor understood it thus: 'Here is the appropriate end for anyone who raises their hand against the People's power.' But there was also another way of looking at it: a likeable guy dies because there's no place for him in this inhuman system that thrusts him out on the rubbish heap.'

Telling stories through images became an advantage when, after the film was made, the director had to go through complicated negotiations with representatives of the Culture Department. Agreement to distribute depended on them. Here one must stress that agreement to distribute a film in Poland was not synonymous with permission for it to take part in foreign festivals. Ironically, censorship itself helped to create the success of the films of this period. The viewer was all the more careful in following the meaning of what was happening on the screen; consciousness that films were very carefully controlled made him/her analyse a film in depth, in order to be able to tell why this or that situation or object occurred in it.

The symbolic image also contributed to international recognition for the 'Polish school', for, thanks to it, the experience of characters against the background of very recent Polish history was not something hermetically sealed to a foreign audience. Wajda recalled he 'continually heard: 'What are they going to understand in it?'... Local events in *Popiół i diament* were shown in such a way that the audience took part in a drama which is possible in another country and in other historical circumstances.' In 1959 Wajda, in secrecy, without informing the authorities, took *Popiół i diament* to the Venice festival, where he received the FIPRESCI prize from the critics. Annoyed by this, representatives of the Party removed him from the cinematography committee. However, the interest that the West showed in Polish cinema meant that artists' authority grew more than that of Party activists, and those artists' ability to say substantive things thus became greater. Their Eastern neighbours, too, approved of them. Andriej Tarkovsky wrote for himself and other Russian directors: 'We were very inspired by the attitude to the truth of life in those films, a poetisation growing out of a photography based on naturalism. In its time this was tremendously important, because the cinema up to then had been so false, all pasteboard... And suddenly filmmakers turned in the direction of pure nature, mud, destroyed walls, towards the faces of actors with make up removed. The image was permeated with a completely different feeling, a different rhythm – that was something very important for us then.'

If we take 1956 as the beginning of the 'Polish school', it lasted only four years. In 1960 filmmakers learnt of the resolution of the Central Committee of the Polish United Workers' Party (PZPR) that the achievements of Polish filmmaking over the last three years did not speak out clearly enough in the cause of socialism and did not fit in with society's educational requirements and the politics of the state, citing an inappropriate understanding of creative freedom, subjectivity and aestheticism – in other words, everything that determined the power of images through which filmmakers spoke for themselves. In this respect, the Polish school of filmmaking referred to the national Romantic tradition.

Summing up the years 1954–61 in Polish film, one must emphasise that the metaphorical concept of the 'Polish school' has up to now remained independent of rigid academic definitions. Film historians still ask themselves: Are we dealing with a myth created by critics, or an authentic artistic movement? A broad notion of the school was widespread in times when artistic technique was subject to limited criteria of acceptability. The scope of this concept became substantially more complex in the world of contemporary art, in a time of programmatic breaking of rules and models, and in which the individual vision is preferred. It is certain, however, that the achievements of the movement are, above all, films of directors born in the 1920s, who received their training in the People's Republic. The films of the 'school' broke with a theatrical manner of acting, and with the model of the 'screenplay' film that had been dominant up to then. All this was abandoned in favour of giving complete responsibility for the final shape of a film into the hands of the director. A drawing on native Romantic tradition (in a broad cultural sense) means that one is tempted to call this movement the 'Polish neoromantic school', to quote Stanisław Ozimek.

The note of reflection on the determinants of the wartime fate of the nation, begun by the 'Polish school,' was taken up almost in parallel in filmmaking in the nations of the USSR and in Hungarian filmmaking in the 1960s. It is generally accepted that the 'school's' period of decline is in the years

1962–1965, when the informal links among its creators broke down. From the second half of the 1960s, this movement became a historical phenomenon. One can, however, speak of the living creative cultural tradition of the 'Polish school', which is most clearly evident in Wajda's films – such as *Wszystko na sprzedaż* (Everything for Sale, 1969), *Krajobraz po bitwie* (Landscape after a Battle, 1970), *Wesele* (The Wedding, 1973), and *Ziemia obiecana* (The Promised Land, 1975).

In the heyday of the 'Polish school', cinema became important in Poland, more important than it was before, or has been since. Its creators held a hope that through cinema the world might become better. Today – though films are still shown in cinemas – this hope is gone. Andrzej Wajda confesses bitterly in his autobiography: 'The world is seriously ill, and although we give it new toys like to a little child – that doesn't cure it.' In comparison to the 1950s, the cinema-going public has radically changed. In the 1980s a repertoire of mainly 'karate films' meant that the intelligentsia stayed away from the cinema. The post-1989 free market completed the job and made Poland like the West. American cinema conquered young audiences, which today make up the majority of the cinema-going public. The free market demands entertainment above all. A reduction of the number of cinemas in the country to 700 meant that there is no single, opinion-forming public. Audiences are eager for every kind of freedom – or rather licence – in behaviour and in politics. Today there are no films for everybody.

Further Reading

Andrzej Wajda, *Autobiografia. Kino i reszta świata*, Warsaw, 2000.

Adam Garbicz and Jacek Kalinowski, *Kino wehikul magiczny. Podróż druga 1950–1959*, Kraków, 1987.

Tadeusz Lubelski, 'Film fabularny,' in *Encyklopedia kultury polskiej XX wieku*. Film. Kinematografia, ed. E. Zajicek, Warsaw, 1994.

Konrad Eberhardt, *O polskich filmach*, Warsaw 1987.

A. Werner, 'Miej serce. O twórczości Kazimierza Kutza,' *Kino*, 2000.

Stanisław Ozimek, 'Spojrzenie na "szkołę polską",' in *Historia filmu polskiego*, ed. Jerzy Toeplitz, vol. 4, Warsaw, 1980.

Darek Foks

Why I am Not a Gravedigger

translated by Barbara Bogoczek and Tony Howard

I'm not a gravedigger, I'm a carpenter.
Why? Perhaps I'd rather be
a gravedigger, but I'm a carpenter. I work

with gravediggers. Here's one:
he starts digging. I study his spade
'Sit down and have a drink' he says. I sit down
and drink. We both drink. I look
at the spade. 'You've got a big lump of clay on that.'
'I knew there was too much of something.'
'Right.' I leave and days pass
and I return. The digging
progresses, and I subside, as do
the days. I come. The grave's
dug. 'And what happened to
the clay?' Only the spade's
left. 'I buried it' he says.

And me? One day I think about
a coffin: made of oak. I'm cutting
planks. And soon I've a whole
plank pile, un-planed.
Then another pile. A plane
would be handy, not the one I use
but a sharp one, able to drew some colour
and life from the wood. Days pass. It's an item
of furniture actually, I'm a real carpenter. I've finished the cutting
but haven't even mentioned
the nailing bit. There are twelve coffins,
I slide them in a van. And one day
outside the cemetery I see a van with spades.

Catherine Czerkawska

Reflections on a Polish Heritage

As Adam Zamoyski says in his history, *The Polish Way*, 'The Poles are the nation who really lost the Second World War.' They suffered equally at the hands of their eastern, as well as their western neighbours. Six million civilians as well as half a million soldiers died. By the end of the war, there were a million orphans, and half a million invalids. They lost homes, land, history, and heritage. And they were well and truly stitched up by the winners. An alarming number of people in the UK today have no idea of these statistics, and things are unlikely to improve as long as the press, to say nothing of the BBC, continue to refer to 'Polish death camps'. Once Hitler had finished with Jews and Gypsies, his intention had always been to move on to the Slavs, whom he regarded with only a little less loathing. In the time available to him, he made a good start.

My grandfather Władysław was a cavalryman from an ancient family of Polish horsemen. He was imprisoned by the Russians early in the war, but when Stalin changed his mind and his allegiance, was released, and left to trek east, along with large numbers of his countrymen, to join the Allied army that was mustering on the border. Before I ever knew that he had made that impossible journey, I would sometimes look at the map of what was then the Union of Soviet Socialist Republics and think how very big it was.

I used to imagine that one day there would be a knock on the door and my unknown grandfather would come walking into the room but he was dead long before I was born.

Over the years, my father had told me about his past. He was always reluctant to speak about the war, but he was much more forthcoming about his childhood. I had even been to Poland, and spent several weeks in a spa town called Ciechocinek, with my great uncle Karol Kossak and his wife Wanda, the only one of my grandfather's siblings to survive the war. Two elder brothers were killed in border skirmishes, and another sister, Ludmilla, died in Auschwitz, where she had been sent because her husband was an Army officer. I've seen a pre-war picture of her, pretty in silk pyjamas, smoking a cigarette in a long thin holder and smiling flirtatiously at whoever was behind the camera.

Later, I realised that I needed to explore these things further, to write a play, perhaps even a novel, with a Polish background. When you set out to write fiction based on fact, there comes the insidious temptation to substitute the considerable work involved in researching the facts for the quite different work involved in a piece of creative writing. Research is the perfect displacement activity. You can visit libraries, buy books, spend hours on the internet, all on the perilous assumption that in assembling these fascinating bits and pieces into some kind of order, you have actually produced a work of fiction and that the truth of such a work is the same as the truth involved in a piece of creative writing.

Most of us have read historical novels in which research has been used as a substitute for literary exploration. This is theme-park fiction where beautifully authentic models in period costume pass before your eyes, but there is an underlying sense of unreality, it's all peculiarly painless and the sound quality is awful. I don't necessarily exempt myself from my own charge here. In fact when I began researching my family history, I found out just how easy it was to dig a large and enticing pit into which it was then possible to tumble.

My 'Polish' play, called *Noon Ghosts*, my attempt to recreate lovely Ludmilla, was produced on BBC Radio 4 some years ago but the novel has been evolving (along with much else) ever since, into its present incarnation. Called *The Sorrel Mare*, it is set in eastern Poland in the turbulent years between 1820 and 1880. I had lived and worked in Poland for a year but still found myself wondering how I could write about people living in a time and place so remote from me as to seem like a fairy tale?

My father came to Yorkshire via Italy, with a Polish unit of the British Army. Before that he had been in a prisoner-of-war camp, and as a boy had acted as a courier for the resistance. He was born in the Polish wild east at a place called Dziedziłów, where his father Władysław had a house, unexpectedly inherited from his great uncle Julian. Władysław married Łucja from Lwów, and my father, another Julian Czerkawski, was born. The marriage was far from happy, and when Julian was ten or eleven, the couple separated. My father sometimes admitted that he would rather have stayed with Władysław in the countryside, but instead he had to go to Lwów with Łucja, only visiting Dziedziłów occasionally.

When war broke out, Julian – in his early teens – was still living in the city with his mother. He remembered that he would have to trek to Dziedziłów to fetch cheese, fruit, vegetables and meat back to Lwow, where food was scarce. By now Władysław was in prison and the house itself had been commandeered by the Russians. Julian's much loved Polish nursemaid was married to a Ukrainian Bolshevik, who could have betrayed him on many occasions. Instead he gave the boy food and shelter, and made sure that he got safely back to the city with as much food as could be spared.

Having survived the war, and reached the UK, Julian had a choice of jobs – he could work in the mills or the mines. He worked as a textile presser in Leeds, while he went to what was known as 'night school'. (Eventually, he was to become a distinguished research scientist.) He met my Leeds Irish mother at a dance. Later, somebody said to her, 'I think they should send all those awful Poles back home, don't you?'

'No', she said, 'Seeing as how I've just married one.'

This was in the early Fifties and he was classed as an 'alien'. Whenever a crime was committed in the city, and the perpetrator was thought to be a foreigner, the police would come hammering on the door in the middle of the night, waking me – a small baby – in the process. At least it relieved some of the perennial pressure on another branch of my family – the Irish immigrants. After this had happened a couple of times, my mother went to the door instead of my more conciliatory father and gave them a tongue lashing. They never came back. Presumably they reckoned that if he had such a strong-minded wife, he wouldn't be out on the town committing alien crimes.

But all this was simply the background to my life. I needed to know more. I began with half a dozen tiny photographs which my father had brought with him, and a handful of very hard facts. I read whatever I could of the history of Poland. I wanted to know how the huge political upheavals of the time had impinged on my own family's history. I also encouraged my father to write a detailed family chronology, complete with sketches of the house where he was born, and the village where he had lived.

The family were part of the old Polish nobility, with a coat of arms and a family tree that stretches back to the fourteenth century. My long lost grandfather seems to have been an eccentric and engaging character, who was born in a sleigh, one icy January night, and continued throughout his short life to live up to this intriguing start. Piece by piece, I began to match family chronologies with what had been going on in the outside world. Once I began to arrange events, filling in dates and times, assessing when something happened and how, I often discovered why something had happened as well.

I found out that my great-grandmother, Anna, had been married at the age of seventeen to a much older man, my great-grandfather Henryk Czerkawski. He had died while his wife was still in her late twenties, killed, as two of his sons would be later, in some border skirmish. He too had been a cavalry officer and this was a very uneasy marchland, much too close to Russia for comfort. Anna was left with five children to bring up. She lived on another Czerkawski estate at a place called Przemyślany, but I knew that my father had been born at Dziedziłów, some thirty miles away. And I knew something else. Anna had – to the disapproval of her children – married for a second time. Quite unexpectedly, she had married her Ukrainian estate manager. Why?

Some research, most of it done by post (this was well before the days of the internet) coupled with more close questioning of my father, brought me some answers. Julian Czerkawski, after whom my own father was named, had been a wealthy man, one of the Polish representatives to the Austro-Hungarian Parliament, and a medical doctor. When he died unmarried and childless, he had left his estate of Dziedziłów to his favourite great-nephew, Anna's youngest son, my grandfather, Władysław.

A little research on birth dates showed me that my grandfather had inherited Dziedziłów when he was only eight years old. An estate manager was employed to look after things until the boy should reach his majority, which explained why Anna became a frequent traveller between Przemyślany and Dziedziłów. The fact that a young widow was thrown together with a capable young man made the subsequent marriage much less surprising. They had a daughter who, after the death of her parents, was brought up in my grandfather's household. My father remembered viewing her as an older sister although she was, in fact, his aunt.

My father's past had always seemed so remote and exotic that I had already, in my daydreams, fictionalised it. My grandfather had a mythical quality, like a hero in a fairytale. The more I began to know about him and his forebears, the more difficult it became to move on to the fiction I was planning to write. To broaden my understanding, I wrote to the *Polish Daily Newspaper*, published in London, asking for information about life in country houses in Poland before the war. I was sent letters, accounts, photographs, all kinds of fascinating information, evocations of a long-dead way of life. These seemed to be exactly what I needed and it was at this point that I took a deep breath and began to write my novel, but it was as if I had to give myself permission to do it, to move from the safe haven of the known chronology to the precarious seas of fiction: a difficult and mysterious process.

Working on *The Sorrel Mare*, which was always intended as the first novel of a trilogy, has been a voyage of unexpected discoveries and I have found help in the most unexpected places. For little or no cost, the Austrian Parliamentary Archive sent me copies of speeches made by Great-Uncle Julian. Libraries in Poland too were obliging with the small means at their disposal. I was even sent copies of Julian's very fulsome obituaries from both the Polish and the Austrian newspapers of the day.

I discovered unknown branches of the family, and relatives in London and in the USA. I found out about a six times married antecedent who had died in a hunting accident at the age of ninety-six and this too supplied me with one of my more satisfying fictional characters. Finally though, I was thrown back into the real world with a jolt when a letter arrived from a previously unknown cousin who was able to tell me what had really become of my grandfather. He must have been utterly debilitated by his spell in prison, because the journey east proved too much for him, and he died of typhus, as did the vast majority of his companions, and is buried in a place called Bukhara, where beautiful rugs were – and probably still are – made. I am told that his grave still has an inscription which reads *Lancer Władysław Czerkawski.* He was thirty-eight when he died.

At one point I also wrote, not very hopefully, to the historical museum in the Ukrainian city now known as Lviv, asking for archive information about my family, since I knew that their estates had been some forty kilometres to the east of that city. A letter arrived from the young museum curator telling me that he would be delighted to travel to my father's birthplace and tell me what he found there. He took some photographs of the house, now used as a nursery, the grounds, the village, even the old ice house. This is what he wrote to me, later, in English, about that journey:

> *I arrived at Didyliv with my friends. The first who we met was an old man. Fancy that he remembered well your grandfather and even your father whom he called Julek! This man told us your grandfather was very kind to the nearby smallholders and helped them to keep farming. Then he told us where to find your grandfather's estate...*

For a complete stranger to find such a connection in a village that had known such upheavals was amazing and I realised that in trying to fictionalise the fact of my own family background, I had also succeeded in making real something that had, for the whole of my life until that moment, seemed as vague as a fairytale and just as fantastic.

Meanwhile, as Poles flood into Britain in ever greater numbers, or so the tabloids tell us, always with that dangerous edge of chauvinism, I remember my dear, wise, unembittered father, his 'alien' status, and the woman who thought they should all be sent back. And sometimes, as when somebody recently asked me which side the Poles had fought on in the war, I surprise myself with the visceral nature of my own reaction to such ignorance.

Signs of Place
1960s Neons, Warsaw

Photographs by Ella Chmielewska

Nowy Świat, 2002 (still in place in May 2007)

Aleje Jerozolimskie, 2002

Ściana Wschodnia, 2002

Moniuszki Street, 2002

Ściana Wschodnia, 2002 (still in place in May 2007)

Świętokrzyska Street, 2002

Reviews

A Book of Lives
Edwin Morgan. Carcanet. ISBN 9781857549188. £9.95
Beyond the Sun: Scotland's Favourite Paintings
Edwin Morgan. Luath Press. ISBN 9781905222728. £9.99

Where to begin? Take a tip from the maestro and begin with an ending that promises a future. 'Conversation in Palestine', the last poem in *A Book of Lives*, has Jesus looking forward to the future demise of all faith-based thinking (he doesn't actually say this, but it's an inescapable consequence of what he does say) and a transformation in the way we address the world. Ludwig Wittgenstein will one day come along with the rigorously anti-metaphysical procedures of what we now call ordinary language philosophy. 'Nothing not based on the ordinary will ever survive', Jesus claims in defence of his prophecy; an interesting proposition to issue from the mouth of a god's son and the memory-laden pen of a poet whose extraordinary leaps, twists and combinations have entertained and provoked us for well over half a century. Still, claims a poem called 'Retrieving and Renewing', commissioned by the Scottish Association of Literary Studies, 'Cosmic circumstance/Hides in nearest, most ordinary things.'

Morgan has spent a lifetime testing his sturdy Scottish empiricism to the limit and beyond. He has also always known that memory is figured as history's daughter because remembering needs a past to work on. So let's remember the ordinary language of the first poem here, 'For the Opening of the Scottish Parliament, 9 October 2004', which was read by Liz Lochhead on the occasion: 'We give you our consent to govern', the poem's speaker says, 'don't pocket it and ride away'. Already his/her advice is returning to haunt our reconvened legislators. 'What do the people want of the place?':

> A nest of fearties is what they do not want.
> A symposium of procrastinators is what they do not want.
> A phalanx of forelock-tuggers is what they do not want.
> And perhaps above all the droopy mantra of 'it wizny me' is what they do not want.
> Amen to that.

An opportune virtue of the loosely interactive sequencing Morgan has perfected over the years in an impressive variety of forms is that additional space can always be found for further reconstructive recall. He first performed the 'Planet Wave' suite with Tommy Smith and the Scottish National Jazz Orchestra at the 1997 Cheltenham Festival, and then a year later in Edinburgh. It is now updated with more poems, notably the challenging elegy of 'Twin Towers'. The first piece in 'Planet Wave', dated '20 Billion BC', gives the Big Bang theory of universal origins a characteristic treatment that discloses cosmic circumstance in an ordinary hand. This centres the body and manages to hold on to empirical dimensions:

> It was as if a fist had been holding fast
> one dense packed particle too hot to keep
> and the fingers had suddenly sprung open
> and the burning coal, the radiant mechanism
> had burst and scattered the seed of everything,
> out through what was now space[.]

'Planet Wave' then projects a witnessing speaker through time and across space to pick out moments and events in the human story and deliver them onto the page in specific detail and with immediate pitch. The strategy makes witnessing speakers of every reader: but illusions of the real are just that; so the figure of the inventing poet is guide and reminder for what happens in the creative act of reading. When beer-brewing cavemen (30,000 BC) get drunk after a successful hunt – 'see mamm'ths? Mamm'ths're fuck'n stupit' – our recording scribe deploys appropriate alienation-effect for firelight shadows cast on the cave wall: 'A deep horn gave that movie flicker its score'.

Together with work that explores the social politics of historical memory, an extended dialogue between Gorgo ('a cancer cell') and his normal potential victim, Beau, adds to a striking group of poems Morgan has written about his condition. Nothing is beyond story: the way he makes music while addressing a terminal threat is a triumph of the imaginative will. All spinning tops eventually stop:

> fall back
> Into silence, attack
> As you will, take the lash as you will, to stave off
> the mundane numbing and dumbing.

That allegorises things, whereas computerised tomography in 'Scan Day' produces a realist mode of representation with no illusions about it: 'there are no chimeras/ under the cameras./ You are laid out as you are, imperfect, waiting, wondering, approximately free.' If there can be such a thing as stoical optimism, the collection's penultimate poem, 'The War on the War on Terror' earns its right to address a woman unwilling to 'bring a child into a world so dreadful': 'I outstare you with my unspoken thought/ That the greatest gift it is possible to make/ is life itself.'

Although this book of lives includes the kind of range we have come to expect: from a personified 'Old Gorbals' through 'Boethius', 'Charles V' and 'Oscar Wilde' to 'Hirohito', the plural dimensions memorialised are ultimately Morgan's own. He was nervous about some of the fifty poems that make up the sequence 'Love and a Life', first published by Mariscat in 2003 and now placed at the heart of a fuller collection. 'At one point,' he told Phil Collins (Arts Editor at *The Herald*), 'I thought I would change the names, but I wanted it to be honest about myself, my life and the people I knew. In the past I couldn't name people. There were penalties for it in the past. It's a new kind of poetry for me.' It's a new lyric form too, one he had invented and tried out in *Cathures* (2002), combining a Whitmanesque free verse long-line effect with rhyme. Finding six rhymes along the same sound while sustaining a long-line rhythmic freedom was, he allowed, 'quite difficult' to get right. Unobtrusive connections link poems whose true combining agent is love in its many guises, straight or gay, remembered or invented, fulfilled or not. 'After a Lecture' involves Morgan's real world feelings for a heterosexual – and so anyway unobtainable – male called Mark whose presence is felt elsewhere in the series. There is a pathos here that contributes to the sense that Morgan is taking stock of his life more generally; looking back at relationships and opening up areas of personal experience.

A Book of Lives includes five of the poems written to accompany paintings chosen in a *Herald* poll as Scotland's favourites. To read all ten of them interleaved with reproductions of the pictures, do yourself a favour and buy the attractively designed and well-produced Luath Press volume *Beyond the Sun*. With an accessible and relevant essay on poetry and painting by Alan Riach, and an afterword by Morgan's successor as Glasgow's Laureate, Liz Lochhead, it deserves a wider readership than poetry usually enjoys. Riach reminds us that Marshall Walker, Morgan's friend and sometime colleague, long ago identified 'the intrinsic optimism of curiosity' as a key quality of Morgan's mind. On present evidence, both the optimism and the curiosity are still up for it.

Colin Nicholson

Walking on Air.
Muriel Spark. The Cahiers Series, 2. Sylph Editions and the Center for Writers and Translators, American University of Paris. ISBN 9780955296314. £10.00

Coming as the second in a series of *Cahiers* that make available new explorations in writing and translating', *Walking on Air* was published in April 2007 to coincide with the concert given at London's Wigmore Hall to mark the first anniversary of Spark's death.

The nine fragments and finished pieces in *Walking on Air* represent various aspects of the process by which Spark 'translated experience into art'. All except two, possibly three, have been published before, so in a sense this collection can be said to herald the beginning of the appearance of Spark's 'literary remains'. The previously unpublished pieces are: 'The Interpretation of Dreams', a fragment; and an account of a dream, the subject of which gives this collection its title. The 'probably hitherto' unpublished piece is a note on Spark's neat version of Horace.

Used in French as a printing term for a gathering of sheets, and also related to the English 'quire', the word *cahier* can, of course, mean notebook, exercise book, or journal, which may suggest something slight or sketchy, or of a lesser importance. Though ethereal in name, there is nothing light-weight about this publication.

The earliest of the published opuscules here – 'The Ormulu Clock' – dates from 1960, and first appeared in the *New Yorker*; the most recent, the poem 'What?' appeared in the *TLS* in 2002. And in the spirit of the age, one was published online. Spark's diary-entries, commissioned in 1996 by the magazine *Slate*, read as kind of 'blog' in which the author extemporises on the process of writing, giving us a glimpse of her papers and notes and into her 'box of short stories in the making'. In one entry Spark, most atypically, makes a slip of the pen, writing 'remand' for 'remission'. But Homer, too, was known to nod. The diary-entries published here are dated July 1996, though Spark scholars will know that online they are dated June. A detail, but nevertheless the stuff on which bibliographers thrive.

As a physical object too, *Walking on Air* is delightful. Aesthetically very pleasing, it is beautifully made, a sewn paperback with dustjacket and orange and green endpapers. Seven colour photographs complement the texts, including one taken by Spark herself, a surreal study of four pairs of legs and feet, which her companion Penelope Jardine describes most loyally as 'original'.

Michael Lister

Selected Poems
Cyprian Kamil Norwid. Trans. Adam Czerniawski. Anvil. ISBN 0856463698. £7.95
They Came to See a Poet
Tadeusz Różewicz. Trans. Adam Czerniawski. Anvil. ISBN 0856463612. £11.95

As a child I never learned more than the most basic Polish, which is a source of regret to me, although I understand the reasons why. My father had lost everything in the war and was struggling to build a new life. Nevertheless, I wasn't totally ignorant of Polish literature. My father was fond of quoting Adam Mickiewicz's epic poem 'Pan Tadeusz', and later, my great-uncle Karol told me about Cyprian Norwid, whose poetry he admired. But I discovered Tadeusz Różewicz by myself, and perhaps for that reason I loved his work best. The fact that these translations were published in 2004 is symptomatic of just how marginalised Polish culture has been, here in the UK, until now.

For many years Norwid was exiled in France and also in America. The idea of home informs much of his work, not just the place, but the spiritual process of exile itself, the unfulfilled longing to be elsewhere. As Bogdan Czaykowski says in his excellent introduction to this edition, 'Norwid's life was in many ways pitiful and it ended in total neglect and oblivion' – so often the fate of those who 'chart a new direction.' Norwid was writing as part of a poetic tradition which he himself seemed determined to reject, always pushing the boundaries of meaning, so that these nineteenth-century poems seem extraordinarily modern to a twenty-first century reader.

Tadeusz Różewicz was born in 1921, and so Poland's horrific experience of war inevitably informs much of what he wrote. He writes with infinite wisdom and a tough appreciation of the human spirit as well as an impatience with aestheticism. The parallels with Norwid, the desire to 'grant objects proper names', are obvious. For both poets there is a sense of the inadequacy of language but Różewicz goes further in his determination to translate everyday life into poetry. *They Came to See a Poet* is Adam Czerniawski's *tour de force* of translation, an extensive collection of Różewicz's work, a retrospective covering the poet's work to the present day.

Of the two, I suspect that Norwid's style may be the more challenging. There is one prose piece, about Chopin, in this collection: a sad, intriguing and unexpectedly funny evocation. Sometimes, however, it seems as if the reader is being presented with a code to which he or she must find the key – and yet it is precisely in this struggle with words and form that the poetry yields sudden and unexpected rewards, as in the short poem called 'Mercy':

When tears flow, they wipe them with a cloth,/ When blood flows, they run up with a sponge,/ But when the spirit oozes under stress,/ They will not rush with honest hands/ Till God dries it with a thunder flash:/ – Only then! ...

The counterpart to Norwid's 'Mercy' may be found in Różewicz's 'Unrecorded Epistle', in which, as Jesus writes in the sand, we hear him saying:

Mother they are so dim/ and simple I have to show them/ marvels I do such silly/ and futile things/ but you understand/ and will forgive your son/ I change water into wine/ raise the dead/ walk the seas

they are like children/ one has always/ to show them something new/ just imagine...

Christ's appeal to his mother, rather than his father, is characteristic. Różewicz is a poet who always values women and 'A Tale of Old Women' is an incantation, a profound evocation of the female as the preserver of all the simple rituals of human survival, the old women who 'rise at dawn/buy meat fruit bread/ clean cook/ stand in the street/ arms folded silent' as opposed to 'dictators' who 'clown/ their hands stained/ with human blood'.
There is so much that is moving in these pages that it seems invidious to select one poem as being most worthy of mention. There are poems which will be familiar to readers from past anthologies, but also many new discoveries, poems which resonate in the mind long after you have read them, sometimes bleak and angry, sometimes loving or funny, terse yet energetic, with a sparse lyricism, always wise, and profoundly Polish. The translations are brilliantly executed. The essential mismatch between Polish and English has been used to brilliant effect by Czerniawski to underline the qualities of each poet. If you want to understand something of the Polish psyche, both of these volumes should be essential reading. But if you must choose one, then let it be Różewicz, who will enchant you with reality and frequently move you to tears.

Catherine Czerkawska

Robert Louis Stevenson and Theories of Reading
Glenda Norquay. Manchester University Press. ISBN 9780719073861. £50.00

The panorama of Stevenson's reading is filled with landmarks and signposts. His enthusiasm for books is a continuous theme, running through his letters and essays and driving his fiction. Glenda Norquay's study examines the relationship between his reading, his writing and his ideas on fiction, and explores the tensions that arose as he moved from the constraints of his Presbyterian upbringing to popularity. In the process, she takes a fresh look not only at Stevenson's work, but at a particularly fascinating period – the latter decades of the nineteenth century – in the history of narrative.

At the heart of her argument is the identification of the 'transgressive reader', who guiltily enters historical and fictional worlds and takes pleasure in the resonance of both action and language, and of the 'literary vagrant', roaming through literature without psychological or emotional hindrance. Norquay argues that both are a product of Stevenson's Calvinist background, and both shaped his views on the role of fiction and its practitioners. His writing, his ideas about writing, and his relationship with his readers, grew out of a tension between the pleasure of reading and the Calvinist stress on the authority of text. The result, says Norquay, was 'highly self-conscious scrutiny of his own engagement with books and that of others'. The way the public engaged with his own books was something that preoccupied him constantly, in terms not just of how well they sold – though sales were of course crucial to his viability – but also of the nature of the relationship between reader, text and writer.

His awareness of that relationship influenced the way he addressed the nature of fiction, the responsibility of the author, and the experience of reading. Norquay ranges widely over his essays, both those specifically concerned with writers and writing and those which more tangentially illuminate her argument, stressing his direct and indirect contribution to emerging debates about literature and the imagination. Stevenson was ambivalent about his own popularity – 'There must be something wrong in me or I would not be popular,' he wrote to Edmund Gosse – and was caught between the need to be rewarded for his craft and unease at selling himself. He famously likened writers to prostitutes.

In the course of this densely argued discussion, Norquay tracks Stevenson's involvement in contemporary debates about realism and romance and their effect on his own writing. Most strikingly, she looks at the way Covenanting history infiltrated his work. Stevenson's fascination with the Covenanters is well documented. In 1866, the two hundredth anniversary of the Battle of Rullion Green, the sixteen-year-old Stevenson published a pamphlet on *The Pentland Rising*, which he researched seriously and widely, and the Covenanters continued to haunt his writing life. Although he wrote the opening chapters of a Covenanting novel, *Heathercat*, he never produced a sustained piece of fiction on a Covenanting theme. But Norquay argues that *The Master of Ballantrae*, a novel that is interestingly hard to categorise, is inhabited by the 'spirit' of the Covenanters and that 'elements of its style, structure and concerns also bear their imprint'.

Norquay writes primarily for the scholar and student, and sometimes her argument feels too strongly concentrated – two books forced into the skin of one? – but it raises issues that direct us to current disquiet about writer popularity and the distortions of the marketplace. It also impinges on concerns about reluctant readers, and the possibility that the experience of reading, the kind of immersion in language and delight to the imagination that Stevenson describes, is being eroded. Earlier this year we saw the UNESCO City of Literature's 'One Book, One Edinburgh' project making available four different versions of *Kidnapped* to readers of all ages throughout the city, accompanied by programmes of talks, events and escapades. Who read *Kidnapped* during this month-long project? Was it read by some who wouldn't otherwise have picked it up? And what can we learn about the relationship between reader and words on the page, between words on the page and the transformations they can engender? Some answers may emerge when the evaluation process is complete.

Stevenson never ceased to be aware of his transgressions as a reader, and never ceased his literary vagabonding. If he was not himself able to write without what Norquay calls 'Calvinist-inflected anxieties', he wanted to offer his readers opportunities for enjoyment. But, as Norquay highlights, he was acutely aware that 'the stylistic delight and psychological pleasure' that the reading experience should entail could not be divorced from 'the material contexts of labour and trade'. More than a hundred years after Stevenson's death, writers and readers still wrestle with the problems embedded in relationships between creativity, audience and marketplace.

Jenni Calder

My Father: Reith of the BBC
Marista Leishman. Saint Andrew Press. ISBN 9780715208342. £19.99

It is nearly seventy years since Sir John Reith abruptly ended his sixteen-year reign as Director General of the BBC, but his legend lives on and his glaring figure looms down from an oil-painting in the foyer of Broadcasting House. The BBC's original mission as set out by Reith was to inform, educate and entertain, in that order. He insisted on standard English pronunciation by his announcers (the BBC accent) and a high moral tone among his staff. He was respected as well as feared – the novel, *The Perfect Witch*, published in 1935 by one of his young producers, Lance Sieveking, portrays him as a benevolent father figure, all-knowing and all-seeing.

Reith had disliked television ever since its appearance in 1926 at the hands of his fellow Scot, John Logie Baird – my father – who had resented him after an unpleasant encounter in their student days at the technical college in Glasgow (as recounted in *Television and Me: The Memoirs of John Logie Baird*, which I edited). But when the two men met in 1931 to discuss support for television, Reith noted in his diary, 'Of course [Baird] saw my point of view, and when I see him he is always reasonable.' From 1929 to 1935, the BBC broadcast experimental television programmes using the original Baird system, but Reith left the arrangements to his underlings and he was not even present at the public opening of the higher definition service in 1936. He lived on into the swinging Sixties as Baron Reith of Stonehaven and at last he grudgingly agreed to appear on television. The subtle skill of the one-to-one interviewers, John Freeman and later Malcolm Muggeridge, showed for the first time that there were cracks in Reith's stern façade.

In her memoir of Reith, his daughter Marista reveals his personality in alarming detail, far beyond the polite probings of Freeman and Muggeridge. The book is put together in alternating sections which give the public part of Reith's life in a larger, and the private life in a smaller typeface, which, however, comprises most of the book. The earnest Reithian ambition, to inform and educate, is most apparent at the end of the book where there are eighteen pages of biographical summaries of those named, even including George V and George VI! The illustrations are informative, and there is an excellent index.

Marista Reith (born in 1932), her mother and her brother each endured demands and impositions more drastic than any that Reith inflicted on his staff at the BBC. For example, when she showed an early talent at the piano, her father forcefully took up the idea that she should become a concert pianist. This created in Marista a phobia of any kind of public performance, even to a small group of guests. It says much for her courage that she later went ahead with her marriage (against frantic opposition by Reith) and succeeded in asserting herself as an independent person. Her book flies in the face of the old Scottish maxim 'aye keep something tae yoursel…' and one has the sense that she is driving away the ghosts of an unhappy past by shining a floodlight on them.

Reith's private life was at odds with his puritanical public image and he was prone to infatuations, from his young manhood into his seventies. This aspect was never even hinted at in his lifetime, but in a documentary shown in April 2007 the BBC went to the trouble to interview one of the objects of his affections, still living quietly in the country. At home, Reith was unpredictable and dictatorial. I winced at Marista's account of her father's savage beating of the family dog, which had committed the offence of keeping him awake; the dog fled and was never seen again.

Although this book has been painful to read, I am reluctant to condemn Reith out of hand. My generation benefited from the BBC's scholarly atmosphere, which persisted long after Reith's departure in 1938. Professionally he stood for something fine that has almost disappeared from today's broadcast programming, appealing as it does to the lowest common denominator. It is sad to read of his tortured personality and the torture that he inflicted on those closest to him. Despite these revelations of personal shortcomings, we should nonetheless respect Reith's life's achievements and mourn the decline of his ideals.

Malcolm Baird

Scarcely Ever Out of My Thoughts: The Letters of Valda Trevlyn Grieve to Christopher Murray Grieve (Hugh MacDiarmid)
Ed. Beth Junor. With a foreword by Deirdre Grieve. Word Power Books.
ISBN 0954918541. £20.00

'My dear don't be pathetic… I'll enclose a stamped envelope so that you will be able to let me know your plans.' This letter from Valda, signed 'sincerely', while staying in Cornwall with her mother and aunts, was written in mid-June 1934. In it, she describes her little boy, James Michael, not yet two years old, who has found a photograph of his father and comes out 'hugging it very proudly and inform[s] us excitably, *That's Daddy! That's Daddy*!'

This one letter encapsulates the three main strands that emerge in reading this collection of letters: that Valda was no doormat; that dire lack of money and continual uncertainty were what she had to live with; that James Michael's love for his father and Valda's love for her son formed the weld that held the three together over the years. And while these are letters written for practical, hurried communication, not in any sense as literature, they vividly convey much of the existential daily reality of Valda's life.

Valda had a strong sense of her own identity. She was lovingly loyal to her Cornish homeland and to her difficult, ageing aunts. She was vehement that her husband should not address her as 'My dearest V', but write her name fully. She herself always wrote out the full name 'Christopher'. She explained when she was 'not prepared to make any more sacrifices' and when she appreciated him and his 'many good points'. She described her ordeals with determined cheerfulness and resilient optimism: 'We'll win through together somehow', she wrote in September 1942 when trying to manage her escape from Whalsay to join her accident-prone husband, who was by then working in a munitions factory in Glasgow. Under no illusions as to Christopher's lack of reliability when it came to money, drink, women, paying debts, and telling the truth, Valda also realised she was 'more unhappy away from you than with you – so that's that'.

This was a woman who created her own life, who could make decisions and carry them out. Her problem was the man she wanted to fit herself around. It was normal for a man to put his work first, not always to remember the birthdays of his wife and children, to expect household duties and childcare to be undertaken by his wife. The other side of the deal was that the husband work to provide for his family. This was not Christopher Grieve's priority. What were continuing debt and hardship in relation to changing the world and writing poetry like a breadknife that cuts through three slices of bread in one? Valda understood this and undertook Herculean tasks of washing, knitting, packing, parcelling and travelling. She nursed her sick child through the extreme dark and cold of a Shetland winter, with no electricity, transport, telephone, domestic appliances or help. She was dependent on the boats coming in through the storms for even the sending and receiving of letters – the only means of communication apart from telegrams. 'I can't help feeling like a rat in a trap', she wrote. Some rat, some trap.

Probably one of the most crucial periods was when Grieve had his so-called 'nervous breakdown' soon after the family settled in Shetland. Valda supported him through this, even when he was diagnosed with syphilis. She wrote, 'I didn't know I loved you so much until you were so ill – it's just great to be able to feel light-hearted again, Hurry up and get back – I'm impatient for you'; and 'I sometimes wish I did not care for you so much. Everything – the Past, Present and the Future – would be so much easier.'

Beth Junor, in her introduction, helps us to understand the sociological-psychological background for the letters, in terms of intellectual and creative life, lack of public subsidies, attitudes to material wealth, revealing how much has changed in these respects even since the death of Grieve in 1978. Light is also shed on the life of Michael Grieve, whose widow, Deirdre provides a delightful thumbnail portrait of the dialectics involved in the story. Word Power Books is to be congratulated in undertaking this unique publication, giving an inside and diagonal view on aspects of twentieth-century Scottish literature.

That MacDiarmid managed to achieve what he did, to contribute to society in the catalytic way he did, was in no small measure due to the courageous, lively, practical, woman he married in Valda. 'Whaur extremes meet' indeed: yo-yoed between Cornwall and Shetland, Glasgow and Biggar, husband and son, creditors and friends, she held the dynamic balance which allowed movement into the next spiral. 'Hugh MacDiarmid' was supported loyally by numerous people. As Christopher Grieve, it was Valda, the 'brave little maid' from Cornwall, who bore the brunt and deserves to bear the gree.

Tessa Ransford

Auld Campaigner: A Life of Alexander Scott
David Robb. Dunedin Academic Press. ISBN 9781903765388. £35.00

The life of Alexander Scott forms a fascinating and intricate weave with the story of Scottish literature in the second half of the twentieth century. Chapter Five of Robb's book, entitled 'Renaissance Man', is doubly suggestive. It hints at both the polyphonic nature of Scott's influence (as poet, playwright, critic, and academic), as well as his spiritual roots, traceable within MacDiarmid's famed revival of the 1920s. As an academic, Scott will be remembered as the founder in 1971 of the world's first and only Department of Scottish Literature, located at the University of Glasgow. Overseeing the subject in its embryonic years, Scott was a key figure in determining the form and content that Scottish literary studies would assume. The arrival of Gray, Kelman *et al* during the 1980s would, of course, compel the re-thinking and re-writing of much of this narrative. However, one cannot doubt that these and other authors' work has blossomed in the intellectual space that Scott in particular toiled to establish in previous decades.

Often the line between biography and hagiography is not as clearly defined as one would wish. Scottish literature suffers from such blurred boundaries perhaps more than most – the cult of Burns being one such case in point. Happily David Robb's biography is just that, a biography. Its subtitle '*A Life…*' acknowledges the fact that others could no doubt recall a very different Alexander Scott. One man's forthright passion is another man's obnoxious arrogance. Robb's book does not attempt to rewrite history in any crude way. The tone is one of balance throughout. *Auld Campaigner* is not any obvious retaliation for the Chair in Scottish Literature which Scott was denied, nor the general lack of critical acclaim his poetry has received in recent years. We might recall Scott's absence from Alexander Moffat's *Poets' Pub* (1981), the famous depiction of the Rose Street poetry scene of the 1960s. Robb's book *is* however extensively researched. The author conducted over thirty interviews with people who knew Scott personally. A result of this is a very human and intimate portrait of the man. Outside the hours of teaching Scott was known for his general absence around the Scottish Literature Department. This apparent lack of commitment was doubtless a factor in the refused Chair. But importantly, it derived from Scott's own self-image. He regarded himself as above all else a poet. Teaching was a practical rather than passionately inspired career choice. His lectures had a declarative style, remaining virtually unaltered throughout a thirty-year professional career.

We learn that Scott's delivery was like someone 'dictating methodically down a very bad phone line.' Biography lives off such anecdotal revelation and Robb's book more than measures up. Such honesty renders other aspects of the book all the more moving. Born in Aberdeen in 1920, like many of his generation Scott would see active duty during the Second World War, landing on Juno beach at Normandy. Awarded a Military Cross for valour, Scott's was a matter-of-fact heroism. He recalled the necessity of being the first on his feet after a heavy shelling: 'If I hadn't stood up first, none of the other buggers would have!'

So, what of Scott's poetry? His work can be read as part of the enduring struggle of the Scottish Renaissance, and the use of Scots in particular. A contrast is provided by the more cosmopolitan energies of contemporaries like Alexander Trocchi, Ian Hamilton Finlay and, of course, Edwin Morgan. The comparison with Morgan remains a compelling one. Colleagues at the University of Glasgow, Morgan's poetic star has risen in direct proportion to how much Scott's has fallen. The language question forms a key part of this discussion. Scott's insistence on Scots stands in marked contrast to Morgan's inclination to embrace new technologies, sound poetry, and the rhythm of the Beats. As a guide to the power struggles and competing factions that defined this period, Robb's book is indispensable. *Auld Campaigner* reaches its full stride in the final chapter and its analysis of Scott's poetry. The pithy 'Scotched' sequence offers a scathing indictment of the modern Scottish nation. 'Scotch Education' ('I tellt ye/ I tellt ye') remains hilariously cutting. It reminds us that far from endorsing a blind nationalism, the Renaissance initiated and legitimated a practice of self-criticism, one that continues to resonate throughout Scottish writing and the study of Scottish writing today.

Matthew McGuire

A History of Modern Britain
Andrew Marr. Macmillan. ISBN 9781405005388. £25.00

The Devil can quote scripture. Blair's 'feral beasts' hit back hard at his farewell speech to the press on 12 June. But what he said was true, even if he was not the right person to say it. Twenty-four hour instant news has resulted in 'a media that increasingly and to a dangerous degree is driven by 'impact'. It is all that can rise above the clamour, can get noticed. Impact gives competitive edge.' Almost alone, Nick Robinson, Andrew Marr's successor as BBC political editor, accepted the concept: 'impact' led to sensationalism, unchecked rumour treated as fact, the breakdown of any clear line between reporting and commentary.

This book certainly goes for impact. The first sentences of the Prologue set the tone.

> The play starts on the afternoon on 28 May 1940, at a meeting of the war cabinet... There are only a few players. There is Winston Churchill who has become the nation's leader only eighteen days earlier. He is seen by most of the Establishment and many Conservatives as a rather ridiculous, drunken, dodgy man with a penchant for wild speeches and silly hats.

Precise dates give a factual credence to the Scarfe-like caricature or colour journalism that then follows. The speeches dismissed as wild by Chamberlainites were based on accurate figures on German rearmament suppressed by the government and leaked to Churchill by Foreign Office and MI6 officials who knew they could trust him not to betray them.

Skipping and dipping through these six hundred-odd pages is great fun, perhaps even (I give a quote for the eventual paperback's blurb) 'a damned good read'. For here is a repository of good old anecdotes about politicians and celebrities, alongside many shrewd comments, 'players' and events; but it is not history. Yes, of course, even the most scholarly histories reflect to some extent the prejudices and personalities of their authors. But 'good' makes some real disciplined attempt to separate the narrator from the narrative. Like the BBC 2 television series he wrote and presented, this is *Marr's History of Modern Britain,* much as William Cobbett's *Rural Rides* became printed as *Cobbett's Rural Rides*, read for his lively opinions rather than for topographical accuracy.

Colour takes up an awful lot of words. And Marr cannot resist the unnecessary adjective: searching for export markets for 'outdated British cars and unsuitable British clothing'; 'a great war broke out between Brown in the Treasury and... Alan Milburn'. He explains very well the complexities of the former European exchange rate mechanism and the political consequences of the UK being forced out of it. But then cometh the colour brush: 'Lamont... perhaps better suited to the Regency than the fag-end of the twentieth century, announced that he had been singing in the bath after the ERM debacle, and later added to the insouciant impression by quoting the Edith Piaf song, '*Je Ne Regrette Rien*'.

Tam Dalyell is 'the most influential' Labour backbencher opposed to the 1978 Devolution Act (forgetting George Cunningham, who moved the wrecking amendment and whipped fellow rebels). Tam sustained himself 'with pockets full of hard-boiled eggs prepared by his house-keeper and a head full of hard-boiled arguments against the break-up of Britain'. All this is funny, but even in a popular history, the reader might expect to be helped by some tables of attitudes to devolution, let alone election results, changing social attitudes, social mobility, further and higher education, economic performance and immigration figures. Marr's publishers can present hard tack figures remarkably simply and attractively in their school books on citizenship and history; but here hard figures are hard to find and, when used at all, are scattered inconsistently in the unbrokenly cheerful or dramatic, over-the-top narrative. Well, not entirely unbroken. There are good period photographs, but also some dodgy captions. For Michael Heseltine, 'The Tories had another blonde who felt the call of destiny'; Joan Littlewood 'hero of the working classes' (so she had wished); and 'Michael Foot', with raised stick, 'the most literate and radical man to lead Labour, points in the general direction of the political wilderness.' Some things that are funny to hear can irritate to read if presented as history.

Marr's judgements are good on the failure of post-war planning, on Suez (the lesson not learnt by Blair that we could never influence America on a big one) and on the liberation of the Falklands – it was a desperate Thatcher gamble that paid off. He has an admirable sense of contingency but very little feel for an unread academic literature on economic and social tendencies and change, relying on relatively few secondary sources instead of popularising the best academic writing. Indeed, he tries to distance himself from it, doing his real abilities less than credit. For instance in the Prologue he is right to revive memories of J.B. Priestley as an observer of English life. Priestley's book about England 'was sneered at and disregarded by university academics and posher writers'. Well, that is a nice populist touch. But then to have Priestley inspiring 'Orwell who famously took the road to Wigan Pier… on foot' is a wild surmise for which there is absolutely no biographical evidence. But it is colourful to link them. Oh, and by the way, not 'on foot', Orwell got there mainly by bus and train.

Have I forgotten that this is the *Edinburgh Review*? So I must say that it was bad luck that the book had to go to press before the May election results, meaning that Marr cannot end by redressing, as he is so well equipped to do, both the under-reporting and the grossly prejudiced reporting of Scotland in the London media (with perhaps a sideswipe at *The Scotsman* for being a main source of prejudice). But he could have discussed the constitutional issue long before that and explained – even mentioned – the vexed Barnett formula, and attempted to explain to majority English readers the balance between democratic accountability and nationalism in the home rule movement (indeed, made clear that there is nationalism as separatism and nationalism as federalism). The brief section on the run-up to 1978 and 1979 has the bold sub-heading: 'The Scots and the Welsh Leave Us Close to Tears'. The 'us' intrigues me. Myself an English immigrant to Scotland, I now see that Andrew Marr has passed over to be a Scottish immigrant in England. The last three sentences of the book make that clear: 'The threats facing the British are large ones. But in the years since 1945, having escaped nuclear devastation, tyranny and economic collapse, we British have no reason to despair, or emigrate. In global terms, to be born British remains a wonderful stroke of luck.' Fair enough, but what do we all or each mean by 'British'? A history should at least discuss and clarify that.

Nonetheless, this book will be read with pleasure, for Marr's ironic tone and ever-present pleasant presence. As in the TV series, he plays up the role of celebrity rather than shrewd and responsible former chief political correspondent at the BBC, or as thoughtful intellectual in radio discussion programmes. He has now become his own story.

Bernard Crick

Sonnets by Giuseppe Gioachino Belli
Translated by Mike Stocks. Oneworld Classics. ISBN 9781847490117 £8.99

The Roman dialect sonnets of Belli (1791–1863) have made a couple of desultory sorties into English, only to disappear as quickly as they came, leaving disappointingly little trace. If the poems are of great interest, the poet himself is fascinating only because of the contrast between the jaunty, jocular, irreverent, often obscene verse he wrote and the staid ordinariness of the man himself. He aspired to bourgeois respectability, perhaps, as Stocks implies, as a reaction to the turbulence he had known in Rome as a boy when the armies of revolutionary France invaded his native city, or when in his more mature years the forces of Italian Unification subverted the peace of Papal Rome.

Anyone coming fresh to his poetry would expect the writer to be a roistering, goliardic Villon, but the reality was humdrum. There are two defining images of him, one in stone and one in biography, and both are phoney. The first is the statue erected in his honour in the Trastevere district, portraying him as admirers would have him, top hat, long coat, slightly rakish air, the quintessential man about town he never was. The other has that element of truth about it which pleases those, such as Anthony Burgess, who wish to attribute to him enigmatic depths he never had. In a novel, *Abba Abba,* Burgess imagines that Belli met John Keats, who was in Rome at the same time, and he delights in the image of Belli working by day as a censor for the Papal government and by night writing anarchic or obscene verse which would have scandalised any censor. He was indeed a theatre censor, and an exacting one, who found much to reprove even in Shakespeare, Rossini and Verdi, but it was a brief spell. As a man, he lived in fear that his poetry would, if the word got out, ruin his standing, so he published only one dialect poem in his lifetime, and frequently, but weakly, gave orders for his output to be burned. He did publish some Italian verse, but its few modern readers dismiss it as stiff and formal, like Burns in English.

Belli has enjoyed posthumous celebrity, particularly among writers, like Dario Fo, who are enthusiastic about the ideal of popular culture. However disrespectful the subjects of his verse, Belli revelled in the rigidity and conventions of the classical, Petrarchan sonnet. Inside that fixed structure, his poems have a snap, a bite, a joyousness and an energy which seem to war with the restrictions of the genre. Mike Stocks strives to reproduce the colloquial vigour of the original, and has himself a fine command of the technique of poetry, paying due heed to rhyme and metre, even if he does not always reproduce the schemes used in the original. Dialect is a problem for the translator, since dialect has a status in Italian which seemingly comparable idioms in what can broadly be called English do not. Stocks has to struggle with the limitations of the standard English he employs and with the sense of twee conventionality which willy nilly it imposes. His bravest decision is to include twelve samples of translations by Robert Garioch into wiry Scots.

He is generous to Garioch, and he deserves the same generous respect himself, so it is probably unfair to put the two side by side, but here goes. Both confronted a whimsical, irreverent piece by Belli entitled 'Judgement Day'. Stocks first:

> Four portly angels, trumpets raised up high,
> will plonk down in the corners at their ease
> and blow their horns, and with a booming cry
> will start to state their business: 'Next up please.'

As a translation it is faultless. The colloquial 'will plonk down' has the right ring to it, and the quartet ends with fine conversational flourish which exactly reproduces Belli's *ffora a cchi ttocca.* Now Garioch:

> Fowre muckle angels wi' their trumpets, stalkin
> till the fowre airts, sall aipen the inspection;
> they'll gie a blaw, and bawl, ilk to his section
> in their huge voices: 'Come, aa yees, be wauken.'

It is question of feel. Here there is a sinewy toughness, a relaxed humour and an energy of spirit which matches exactly the voice and tone of Belli. Garioch takes the liberty of adding the 'sall aipen the inspection' which is not there in Belli, but his is a translation and not a mere parallel text, unlike many of the translations which come as an appendix to Burgess's short novel.

The comparison is not meant to patronise Stocks, who at his best displays great brio and panache, and who is always a splendid guide around Belli's work. The quartet and tercet on either side of the *svolta* of another eschatological sonnet, given the title 'The Damned', catch the flavour and curious whimsy of an idiosyncratic and decidedly erotic reflection on what happens in hell when men and women are allowed to mingle in unrestrained freedom:

Now then, imagine what takes place with these
damned folk, who lack all common decency:
there's kicks and punches and – believe you me –
shockers of every kind, like pregnancies!

Yes pregnancies – what else is there to say,
knowing that on the fateful Judgment Day
you're taken with your little box of tricks.

What is the man about? Is Belli merely playful, happy to twist any topic in accordance with a wayward humour of his own, or should we – unlikely – be on the lookout for some deeper purpose? The closing lines contain a jibe at the Cardinal charged with attending to the moral wellbeing of the Eternal City, but who would find the disciplining of the damned in the pell mell of hell beyond him. Everything is grist to Belli's endlessly grinding mill, and it is this eccentric vision that is so beguiling. 'What Does the Pope Do?' he asks in another poem, suggesting that putting in his time must be something of a problem for a man who is reduced to taking coffee, staring out the window over a city which is totally his, and who will never have kids to bother him. Elsewhere, Belli writes, without any undue compassion, of the fate of a would-be assassin of the King of France. His shot missed the King and his children but blew to bits 'the heads and chests and bellies' of innocent bystanders. 'Surely we see the hand of God in this!' he concludes, in a final line of devastating, ironic power.

Roman life passes in array before his eyes – elderly prostitutes, mothers doting on their babies, condemned murderers, pompous clerics, impoverished families and, once, two Highland chieftains who were presented to the Pope in all their tartan finery. Belli, who seems to have known what Scotsmen wear under their kilts, wondered in a sonnet what might have happened had a gust of wind blown through the Papal chambers, kicking up the kilt. It is a good summing up of a quixotic poet who aspired to be a gentleman in public.

Joseph Farrell

Soirbheas/ Fair Wind
Meg Bateman. Polygon. ISBN 9781904598923. £9.99
Dannsam Led Fhaileas/ Let Me Dance with Your Shadow
Martainn Mac an t-Saoir. Luath Press. ISBN 9781905222575. £8.99

Meg Bateman's new book shows her branching out from the short, polished poems that characterised her first two collections. While the Bateman of *Òrain Ghaoil* (1990) and *Aotromachd agus Dàin Eile* (1997) is still visible in many of these poems, here she moves from the highly personal style of her earlier work to a more thoughtful, contemplative kind of poetry. 'Ealaghol: Dà Shealladh' ('Elgol Two Views') describes the speaker's reaction to seeing a postcard showing Elgol in Skye. As is often the case in Bateman's poetry, the second stanza undercuts the first, as the speaker's romanticism is laughed off by a local man whose knowledge of the place and its history is much more concrete. Elsewhere, in 'Ceòl san Eaglais' ('Music in Church'), Bateman argues that imperfection in art is an important and valuable reflection of human experience: 'Ach is annsa leam an coithional nach seinn ach meadhanach – / an seinneadair nach buail air na puingean àrda,/ an tè a cheileireas os cionn nan uile,/ an t-òrganaiche a thòisicheas air rann a bharrachd' ('But best I like indifferent singing,/ the soloist who gets the high notes flat,/ the warbler who makes herself heard over all,/ the organist who embarks on an extra verse'). This poem provides an apt summation of Bateman's apparent ambition throughout this book. On the whole the tone is restrained, quiet and markedly less intense than some of the poetry of frustrated desire that Bateman became known for in the 1990s.

Martainn Mac an t-Saoir's *Dannsam Led Fhaileas* is a very different kind of book. Known to Gaelic readers as the author of the prize-winning short story collection *Ath-Aithne* (2003) and the novel *Gymnippers Diciadain* (2005), Mac an t-Saoir's first book of poems provides further evidence of his versatility. His poetry, unlike that of many of his contemporaries, has a strong relationship with the conventions of traditional Gaelic song, and he demonstrates his abilities in the composition of regular, song-like verse in poems such as 'Màthair a' toirt a pàiste às an eaglais' ('Mother taking her child out of church') or 'Tàladh Iain Fhionnlaigh' ('Iain Fhionnlaigh's Lullaby'). But Mac an t-Saoir is also a moderniser, both in his contribution to the ongoing development of Gaelic free verse, and in the linguistic range of his poetry, exploring the riches of traditional Gaelic vocabulary and syntax, and adding to them through the use of the compound words that are a feature of his work in prose. In 'Air chuairt leat, Eideird Dwelly' ('Travelling with you, Edward Dwelly'), addressed to the author of the standard dictionary of modern Scottish Gaelic, Mac an t-Saoir alludes to the combination of scholarship and spontaneity that is in evidence in the best of these poems: 'Siubhlaidh mi gu tur trod mheuran rianal,/ duilleag a rug duilleach.// Lenaidh mi gu dlùth do fhreumhan saora,/ bun a thuislich briathran.' ('I lose myself completely in your ordinary branches,/pages that bore foliage.// I follow closely your open lines of enquiry,/ root that released eloquence.')

The majority of the poems in both these collections are accompanied by English translations, provided in both cases by the author. One of the more regrettable consequences of this practice is that it has the effect of levelling differences both between writers and across the work of individual writers. Mac an t-Saoir's collection suffers most from this process, because of, rather than in spite of, the range of styles he deploys in his Gaelic poems. The English versions in both books seem trapped between two roles: that of acting as a gloss to the Gaelic poems and of standing as poems in their own right. A more satisfactory solution to the problem of bringing Gaelic poetry to a wider audience might be arrived at by following the example of Ireland, where bilingual collections are often made by having other poets provide the translations, sometimes working from a crib. This takes away from the authors of the original poems the dilemma of having to choose between faithfulness to their Gaelic texts or creating new poems that read well in English. These two collections, as well as providing much that Gaelic-speaking readers can enjoy, also provide ample evidence that such would-be translators will find plenty to work with among the branches of contemporary Gaelic poetry.

Niall O'Gallagher

Like Something Flying Backwards: New and Selected Poems
C.D. Wright. Bloodaxe. ISBN 9781852247621. £12
From Blossoms: Selected Poems
Li-Young Lee. Bloodaxe. ISBN 9781852246983. £8.95

C.D. Wright's third published collection of poems, *String Light*, concludes with a series of 'Ozark Odes', the last of which explains, 'Why I come here: need for a bottom, something to refer to;/ where all things visible and invisible commence to swarm.' Wright is a unique and metamorphic voice in contemporary American letters. Still, no matter how wildly (excitingly) different each of Wright's eleven collections has been, they have always returned to this place she examines at the close of the 'Ozark Odes'.

Wright has ever remained, if not a writer of American Southern dialect as such, one whose poetry is overtly informed by the musicality of Southern diction and the earthiness of Southern aphorism. There is often something deeper, more primal, at work that Wright acknowledges as well in 'those dark arkansas roads that is the sound/ I am after the choiring of crickets.' These are the constants of Wright's many-headed opus: the heard and the unlistened-to. The resultant poetry can be flush with carnality and delivered with a journalistic candidness (as in the poems of *Just Whistle*), or drenched in Southern idiom, then internalised through jagged syntax. For this latter style, read *Deepstep Come Shining*, a book-length poem resembling a road-trip through the Southern States. Included in its entirety here, *Deepstep...* is the jewel of this compilation.

In truth, it is the very composition of this retrospective that marks it as a standout. Considering Wright's stylistic variety, one would think it extremely difficult to weave newer poems in amongst the older ones, but that's exactly what's been done, creating a more cerebral retrospective with something like a pervading narrative structure. The payout is phenomenal, especially when one steps from the last page of *String Light* into the family-historical, dialect-driven long poem 'A Farm Boy', where Wright, subtly riding the collection's underlying current, reinforces the inspirational strength of her origins.

Like Something Flying Backwards is the sort of new-and-selected compilation that gives no impression of having been cobbled together in order to resell the poet's early work. Perhaps Wright's poetry simply does not allow for such a thing. By the same token, it is difficult to do such work justice in so few words. This much, at least, can be said of C.D. Wright: hers is a truly inimitable voice, one that should not go unnoticed by any lover of poetry.

In his debut collection, Li-Young Lee states, 'My father would be ashamed of me./ Not because I am forgetful,/ but because there is no order/ to my memory, just a heap/ of details, uncatalogued, illogical.' While others have been more widely anthologised, this poem, 'Mnenomic', is the quintessential Lee poem for its thematic treatment, its conversational intimacy, and the quiet austerity of its language. *From Blossoms* offers an introduction to this distinctive American voice through a selection of the author's three previous volumes of poetry, accompanied by excerpts from his memoir.

Lee claims, in the poem which opens his second collection, *The City in Which I Love You*, that 'memory revises me,' and it's precisely this revision that we see enacted in the course of *From Blossoms*. Out of the tenderness and trepidation of his first poems, Lee develops the use of ellipses and unfinished sentences in his follow-up volume to signal a growing frustration and uncertainty with memory and with adult life. His third collection, *Book of My Nights*, brings the author full circle, with a voice that is not unquestioning, not without a touch of anxiety, but that is also expressive of a greater, hard-earned confidence. Lee is a master of tone, and the control he exhibits over the measure of his conversational lines is remarkable even in his debut collection. It is this control that has always made Lee's voice so notable in its ability to draw any reader immediately and wholeheartedly into his sympathies.

From Blossoms falters slightly in its composition. Extracts from *The Winged Seed: A Remembrance*, Lee's memoir, are intriguing for what the prose elaborates about his poetics: the careful rein he apparently keeps his use of metaphor under, for example. However, the memoir excerpts are used to preface the poetry in a manner which seems to denigrate them to a sort of glorified biographical note. The deeply personal nature of both the poetry and the memoir (in its own right moving, exciting, and beautifully articulated) would almost certainly have been more artfully preserved had the memoirs been interspersed with the poetry, or else left out altogether. Amid the deft control of Lee's writing, any slippage is noticeable, and with that in mind, this collection should have stuck to the 'Selected Poems' that its cover advertises.

Stephen Lackaye

My Wife's Lovers
John Herdman. Black Ace Books. ISBN 9781872988771. £9.95

With a career verging on forty years, John Herdman is one of Scotland's writing veterans. Staying power does not come by accident, and all the hallmarks of Herdman's experience are on display here – his ability to evoke laughter from serious subjects, to display erudition without alienating his readers and to deal at once passionately and delicately with powerful material, lending an overriding sense of craftsmanship to his work.

On the whole, *My Wife's Lovers* is an enjoyable journey – and travel is a recurring theme here – through history, through Scotland, and through the mind of an intriguing author. At first glance, these stories do not necessarily seem to fit together, but the title of the collection – and the story from which it draws its name – serves as a fitting legend for this disparate map: the known is not necessarily so well-known, and the roster of past lovers of your most beloved may include names and people you would never have suspected. So too with Herdman's fiction. The stories that populate this book, although diverse, tie back into some very elemental themes: of isolation, of self-doubt, of ageing and ultimately, of death. The journeys written about here are not just physical, but emotional, chronological and philosophical.

There is, inevitably, some unevenness in this literary itinerary. The stories in general tend to end abruptly – not inappropriately – with the characters at a crucial juncture in their journey, driving home to the reader quite firmly the significance of the events in the narrative. However, 'Voyaging' and 'Tom na Croiche' are truncated almost to the point of being incomplete; perhaps it is no coincidence that both have a flavour of the autobiographical. Life, after all, is not easily compartmentalised. The scattered historical narratives in 'Voyaging' do not quite hang together as a coherent whole, and are unable to be tethered by the final line cast by the author. 'Tom na Croiche', on the other hand, has the narrator pursuing one storyline and ending somewhere altogether different. Although true to life in that we cannot always be certain to find the answers that we pursue, the change of course left me feeling unsatisfied.

The overall quality of the collection, though, is enough to carry the reader through any rough patches. One of the author's great strengths is to defy expectations, to change gear; each new story presents a very distinct charm. From 'The Burning Curate', which maintains an air of credibility in the face of decidedly absurd happenings, to the hauntingly personal love story, 'Death and Devolution' – which works on both an individual and nationalistic level – Herdman traverses an impressive stylistic, linguistic, and emotional range.

Indeed, it is emotion that is the most compelling ingredient here. Behind the meticulous prose, the clever turn of phrase and the engaging characters, the author's passion for Scotland is matched by his genuine empathy for the struggles of men and women. And even though he approaches much of his subject-matter with a light-hearted tone, Herdman does not shy from difficult resolutions. In 'The Owl of Soilluc', a holiday-goer in his twilight years falls to his death in an attempt to reclaim the merest glimpse of his lost youth. Likewise, 'My Wife's Lovers' leaves us alone at the end with a disingenuous biographer who is able to rationalise the deaths – in which he may or may not have been instrumental – of two individuals, against the greater good of knowledge gained.

Yet the highlight of *My Wife's Lovers*, in terms of sheer enjoyability, has to be 'Cruising', a deceptively innocent, almost fable-like prose interpretation of Herdman's play of the same name. All the vividness that recommends this tale to stage production is preserved. A folksy lesson in morality which plays games with societal divisions and conventions, the story is surreal yet plausible. It is similar to 'Plaintiff' – a less believable journey through a fairy realm – which flips the world on its head for a short time before normal service is resumed. Where John Herdman is concerned, normal service is a high standard indeed.

Andy Gloege

Riptide: New Writing from the Highlands and Islands
Eds Sharon Blackie, David Knowles. Two Ravens Press. ISBN 9781906120023. £8.99

A collection which features writers who for the most part are not widely known, holds at least one advantage over books produced by authors and publishers with established reputations: expectations among its potential readers will be more or less neutral. Compiling the collection with respect to geography, of course, might encourage the reader to presume familiarity, but for *Riptide*, the place in question suggests no firmly established literary context.

What is writing from the Highlands and Islands? If we disregard certain smaller sites renowned for literary activity (like Orkney with its writing through the ages) it's clear that critics haven't conceived of the whole region as a literary unit, yet; they haven't explained it to us. Let's be thankful – the reader can approach this work all the more directly. The writers featured in *Riptide* certainly deserve to have their work judged on its own merits, not in relation to any previous works or notions of overarching traditions. Indeed, the editors seem to ask it, when they highlight the deliberate absence of any common unifying theme 'other than quality'.

Two Ravens Press, established only last year, has worked with twenty-nine writers from north and north-west Scotland (including editors Blackie and Knowles, who contribute short stories) to produce a diverse collection of prose and poetry that is by turns lively, entertaining and serious, as well as capable of moving and challenging the reader. Certain contributors achieve remarkable quality and it's clear that among them are dedicated artists.

Those setting the highest standards include Cynthia Rogerson, whose small town scenario for the short story 'Instead of Beauty' is recognisable universally, yet could also arise only in the Highlands. The central character, Addie, 'gives up on love' and turns to the fish-man, Joe, to try and become pregnant. Rogerson achieves an impressive fluency of narrative voice during the quick seduction, stepping deftly from exasperation to sadness to joy, with characters that both feel essential and real.

'Nil Sorski and the Walrus' by Clio Gray is a gem of another sort – a murder/robbery mystery. When and where the story takes place is only the first puzzle. The narrator has had his ears cut off as punishment for theft, but treats this and further esoteric subject matter without any sense of its peculiarity. Apparent digressions continue to complicate matters right up to the end, even while revelations tumble out, not with any clunking or because they eventually must, but in the course of the telling.

There is notable short fiction from Peter Urpeth and Eva Faber, too. Urpeth's introspective, methodical feel in 'The Clearing' sharpens his fable's tone of lingering sadness. Faber's young narrator in 'Something Perfect in Between' relates painful childhood memories – her lack of self-pity and child-like capacity for accepting hard facts without censure or fear is fully convincing.

A further ten short stories add depth and variety to the collection. However, these either tend to achieve a quality which they then betray (however briefly) in some other aspect or fall short of the high standards set elsewhere.

In contrast, if we turn to the ten *Riptide* poets, we come closer to uniform success. Pauline Prior-Pitt, in 'Shore Sequence', exhibits an overriding concern with colours and objects before her – the sea and sky – to the near exclusion of even her own presence from the page. There is no punctuation or capitalisation – only, it seems, a serious commitment to make her words alone serve the prior fact of nature. The natural world resonates strongly throughout this collection (unsurprisingly, amidst writers who dwell outside larger settlements) and this is only one clear statement of profound sympathy with it. Another is the opening poem, 'That Headlong River', both spiritual and humorous, by Andrew Greig.

Riptide contains numerous texts which fall somewhere between the short story and poetry. We might call it 'microfiction' or the very short story. As a form, it is open to abuse, even finding its way into print sometimes just because of its size. Here, thankfully, John Glenday, Daibhidh Martin and, to a lesser extent, Angus Dunn (in 'Three Short Texts') mould it to fascinating ends. Martin's characters live out a joyous openness to external life-changing influences and events. Glenday's experimental, untitled piece is beautifully crafted and conceived.

The writing in *Riptide* falters in places, but this does not detract from the impact of its most accomplished contributions: instead, these tend to complement the very good writing that exists abundantly elsewhere. This was surely intentional on the editors' part – they are presenting frequently published writers alongside newcomers and, despite its variety, the collection feels solid and coherent.

Alasdair Gillon

Day
A.L. Kennedy. Jonathan Cape. ISBN 9780224077866. £16.99

A.L. Kennedy is of the opinion that of all Powell and Pressburger's films *The Life and Death of Colonel Blimp* perhaps comes 'closest to reaching the unreachable and catching it in the spaces between its words'. These words she wrote ten years ago, but in many ways her fifth novel, *Day*, takes off where her analysis of *Blimp* concluded. Containing both flashbacks to World War II and to a film-set location, *Day* tells the story of Alfred Day, former prisoner of war and tail gunner, who volunteers to work as an extra on a PoW film in 1949. Finding himself lost in the peace, racked by loss and impossible longing, Day returns to a fake war in his fumbling search for catharsis.

Although the canon of fictional books about the Allied experience of World War II is substantial to say the least, A.L. Kennedy brings her independent and highly original voice to bear on what is a difficult genre to get right. As personal memories of the war fade, it is increasingly packaged using hindsight – either as a chunk of history with context but little emotion, or as a surreal metaphor for the horror and insanity of man. Kennedy strips the Second World War of packaging, portraying it as both real and surreal, a matter of precision and pantomime: a thing that immolates hope and offers opportunity. Her hero is an Everyman character like Ivan Denisovich, who is swept up by an extraordinary chain of events. Day is not quite as 'biddable and sensible and ordinary' as he seems. He only calls himself a 'nobody' to annoy a character called Vasyl, who believes, with sinister conviction, that people 'hold blood – that's all they are'. Day is rather more than a bag of flesh or blood or a film-set fiction – he is a kind and loyal man whose wartime odyssey rips at the very seams of his existence.

Kennedy's portrayal of the dark and depressing is well-documented, but her thrust, in this book at least, is more to do with living and loving. When Day first meets his girlfriend, Joyce, she is carrying Homer's *Odyssey*, apparently out of character, for she is 'a bit of a dummy'. This may be a cute piece of false modesty, because she tells Day about the extract, 'where Circe turns them into pigs', before hastily reassuring him that Odysseus 'gets home safe in the end, gets the girl and so forth'. This may be a minor exchange, but the RAF bomber crew have previously made a macabre joke about being pigs, because enemy fire can turn them into pork, whilst miraculously Day does, eventually, get his girl. Kennedy may mute her sense of humour in *Day* – war is not so very funny, after all – but she is a fiercely literary writer whose smallest gesture can reverberate with wit and promise.

An assured stylist, Kennedy regularly shifts from the third to first to the difficult second person perspective, as well as inserting italicised first-person commentary, flashbacks, dialect and songs. Such techniques capture the fragmented and disintegrating mind of Day, 'shut in a kind of private uproar'. It is to the dark corners of his psyche that Kennedy ventures – to the things he carries around but cannot really say in words or show by action. Such technical virtuosity makes the novel, at times, a difficult read. Day is young, naïve and damaged, and the world he inhabits is a place of tight spaces and splayed meaning. However, Kennedy's language often has a beauty and weightlessness that provides a counterpoint to this claustrophobia. Her dark humour also helps: Day's friend Pluckrose introduces him to fellow RAF types as 'usefully short' because he can squeeze into a Lancaster's tail, and his bomber crew pretend the war was caused by Britain stealing penguins from the Eskimos. In the midst of his crew, Day, nicknamed the 'boss', finds a sense of belonging, something he was deprived of at home by his aggressive and possibly murderous father.

Kennedy is a fearless writer, pulling together the casual, daily horror and the tender lives of people 'who will stand at the edge of important pictures'. Nearly everyone encountered in the novel is displaced into different and demanding roles as buildings collapse around them and people die. 'You are a small, soft thing and the world is full of fire and hardness,' writes Kennedy in that elusive, intimate second person. History for a moment is forgotten as she gestures towards a world both monstrous and familiar.

Hannah Adcock

Notes on Contributors

Hannah Adcock is a freelance writer who writes for both the national and regional press. Her first book, *Twentysomething: The Ultimate Survival Guide* (Discover Press, 2004) was published when she was twenty-three.

Anna Bikont and Joanna Szczęsna are journalists for *Gazeta Wyborcza*, Poland's largest daily newspaper. In the 1980s, under martial law, they co-edited *Tygodnik Mazowsze*, the principal underground journal of Solidarity in Poland, and in 1989 they were among the founders of *Gazeta Wyborcza*. Their recent works include *My z Jedwabnego* (We From Jedwabne, 2004, with Bikont as the primary author), a biography of Wisława Szymborska (2003) and two volumes on limericks and epitaphs. 'A Belligerent Voice in Defense of Peace, or Europeans in Wrocław' is a chapter in *Lawina i kamienie, Pisarze wobec komunizmu* (The Avalanche and Its Stones: Writers Facing Communism), which evolved from a series of articles written for *Gazeta Wyborcza*.

Will Brady was born and raised in Kent. He studied literature and art and in 2004 co-founded a bookshop on the Greek island of Santorini. Having since relocated to Edinburgh and completed a postgraduate thesis on the American author Raymond Carver, he now works as a freelance writer, photographer and graphic designer.

Ella Chmielewska is a Warsaw-born Canadian urbanist, photographer and designer. She teaches cultural and visual studies at the University of Edinburgh. Her research focuses on urban iconosphere as a medium of cultural identity and photography as a research method. She has published on graffiti, logos and branding, and urban visual landscapes of Montreal and Warsaw. The photographs in this volume are part of her work for the exhibition *FIAT LUX! Cold War Neons, Modernity and the Metropolis.*

Catherine Czerkawska has written poems, novels, short stories and plays including *Wormwood*, *The Price of a Fish Supper* and *Burns on the Solway.* Her novel, *The Curiosity Cabinet* (Polygon 2005), was a finalist for the Dundee Book Prize; *God's Islanders*, about the history and landscape of Gigha, was published by Birlinn in November 2006. Catherine's website is at www.wordarts.co.uk.

Adam Czerniawski was born in Warsaw and lives in Wales. His publications in Polish include poetry, fiction, essays and translations of English language poetry; publications in English include a memoir, *Scenes from a Disturbed Childhood*, translations of Jan Kochanowski's *Treny*, Cyprian Norwid's *Selected Poems*, Tadeusz Różewicz's *They Came to See a Poet*, Wisława Szymborska's *People on a Bridge* and Leopold Staff's *An Empty Room*; translations of his own poetry, *The Invention of Poetry*, are by Iain Higgins.

Jacek Dehnel, poet, translator, novelist and painter, is a graduate of Warsaw University. His poetry collections include *Parallel Lives* (2004) and *A Trip South* (2005), and he has written two books of short stories, *The Collection* (1999) and *The Marketplace in Smyrna* (2007). His first novel, *Lala* (2006), tells the story of his grandmother's life. In 2005 he won the Koscielski Prize and in 2006 he was awarded with Paszport 'Polityki' Prize. He lives in Warsaw.

Desirée Elfström studied journalism at Sodertorns Hogskola in Stockholm, Sweden and took a BA degree in visual communication at Edinburgh College of Art. As a photographer she has covered cultural events in various countries and is currently working on assorted documentary projects based in Scotland as well as in Turkey.

Darek Foks (1966) is a poet, writer and editor. His debut collection, *Poems on Barbers* (*Wiersze o fryzjerach*, 1994), received an award from *bruLion* magazine. Other publications include *Masterful Lament* (*Misterny tren*, 1997), *Sonnet of the Road* (*Sonet drogi*, 2000), *Overestimation of Maps* (*Przecena map*) and *Decisions from Maastrich* (*Ustalenia z Maastricht*).

Merryn Glover was born in Kathmandu and grew up in Nepal, India and Pakistan. After a teaching degree in Australia she moved to Scotland, working in community arts, before returning to Nepal to teach at an international school. She now lives with her husband and two sons at the foot of the Cairngorms and dreams of Asia.

Paweł Huelle is a novelist, playwright and newspaper columnist. After graduating in Polish studies from Gdansk University in the early 1980s he worked as a press officer for Solidarity. He lectured in philosophy and later became head of Gdansk's local television channel. His acclaimed first novel, *Who Was David Weiser?* (Bloomsbury, 1991), has appeared in many languages and as a full-length feature film. *Mercedes-Benz* (Serpent's Tail, 2005) was shortlisted for *The Independent* Foreign Fiction Award 2006. He has published several collections of short stories, including *Moving House and Other Stories* (Bloomsbury, 1994), as well as screenplays, sketches and essays. His latest novel to appear in English is *Castorp* (Serpent's Tail, 2007).

Jerzy Jarniewicz is a Polish poet, translator and literary critic, who lectures in English at the universities of Lodz and Warsaw. He has published eight volumes of poetry, six critical books on contemporary British, Irish and American literature (most recently a study of Philip Larkin), and has written extensively for various journals, including *Poetry Review, Irish Review* and *Cambridge Review*. He is editor of the literary monthly *Literatura na Świecie* (Warsaw) and has translated the work of many novelists and poets, including James Joyce, Philip Roth, Edmund White, John Banville, Seamus Heaney, Craig Raine, Simon Armitage.

Michał Lachman is a Lecturer in English and Irish Drama at the Department of Drama, University of Lodz, Poland. His research interests include the history of twentieth-century British and Irish drama, literary theory and translation. He has published on Brian Friel, Martin McDonagh, Sarah Kane, Mark Ravenhill and Howard Barker.

Nick Laird has received many awards, including the Rooney Prize for Irish Literature, the Ireland Chair of Poetry Prize, the Jerwood Aldeburgh Award and the Betty Trask Prize. He has published two poetry collections, *To A Fault* (Faber, 2005) and *On Purpose* (Faber, 2007); and a novel, *Utterly Monkey* (Fourth Estate, 2005). A second novel, *Glover's Mistake*, will be published in spring 2008. He lives in Rome. (A poem by Nick Laird, 'Everyman', was printed in *Edinburgh Review* 120 with a section wrongly repeated; to remedy this error, we have reprinted it, with apologies.)

Agata Masłowska has a degree in English Literature from Jagiellonian University, Krakow. She is studying theatre and literature in Edinburgh and is currently writing songs for her newly founded band, The Sprouting Twigs.

Krystyna Miłobędzka was born in Margonin. She has published eight books of poetry. Her collected poems, *Gathered 1960–2005*, appeared in spring 2006. She is involved in children's theatre and theatre for children. She also writes plays.

Ian McDonough is a Scottish poet. His latest collection *The Vanishing Hitchhiker* was published by Mariscat in 2006. His first full collection, *Clan MacHine* (2002), was shortlisted for the Saltire First Book Prize.

Tadeusz Pióro has published six books of poetry in Polish. A selection in English, *Infinite Neighbourhood*, was published by Equipage in 2000. He is the co-editor and principal translator of *Altered State: The New Polish Poetry*, an anthology published by Arc in 2003. His translations into Polish include poems by David Gascoyne, Rod Mengham and Christopher Meredith. He teaches American literature at the University of Warsaw.

Ian Revie teaches Film Studies and French at the University of Edinburgh. His poetry has been published on both sides of the Atlantic in reviews including *Leviathan Quarterly*, *Atlanta Review*, *Orbis* and *Crannog*. A first collection, *The Walrus Tusk and the Dancing Bear*, was published by Akros Press in 2002. He was part of the group who refounded the (then) *New Edinburgh Review* in 1968.

Dilys Rose lives in Edinburgh. She writes mostly fiction and poetry but also enjoys creative collaborations. She has published ten books, most recently *Lord of Illusions* and *Selected Stories*. A new collection of poems, *Bodywork*, is due in autumn 2007.

Tadeusz Różewicz, a highly regarded and influential Polish poet who emerged after World War II, developed his radically austere poetic language out of his wartime experiences in the Polish Resistance.

Laura Solomon was born in New Zealand and now lives in London. She has published two novels in New Zealand: *Black Light* (1996) and *Nothing Lasting* (1997). Her plays include *The Dummy Bride* and *Sprout*. Short stories published in the UK include 'Sprout', 'The Most Ordinary Man in the World' and 'Alternative Medicine'.

John Stape, Research Fellow in St Mary's University College, Strawberry Hill, London, edited *Notes on Life and Letters* and *A Personal Record* for the Cambridge Edition of Joseph Conrad and has co-edited vols 7 and 9 of *The Collected Letters of Joseph Conrad*. He is the editor of *The Cambridge Companion to Joseph Conrad* and Contributing Editor of *The Conradian: The Journal of the Joseph Conrad Society* (UK). His latest book is *The Several Lives of Joseph Conrad* (William Heinemann, 2007).

Wisława **Szymborska** is a poet from Bnin in Poland. Her very early poetry reflects her love of Stalin and his wonderful works. Mercifully, she moved on to write the intelligent, witty poems that won her the Nobel Prize for Literature in 1996.

Magdalena Tulli won Poland's prestigious Koscielski Prize with her first book, *Dreams and Stones* (1995), published in English translation by Archipelago Books in 2004. *Flaw*, her fourth book, will be published in English by Archipelago in autumn 2007.

Elżbieta Wiącek is a lecturer in the Institute of Regional Studies at Jagiellonian University, Krakow. She specialises in the fields of audio-visual communication, art history, cultural semiotics and postmodernism. She has published *Less Attended Ways to Paradise* on Jim Jarmusch's films and *The Film Journeys of Abbas Kierostami*.

Wojciech Wilczyk is a photographer whose essays on fine arts and photography appear in Polish newspapers. He has published two volumes of verse: *Steppenwolf* (1997) and *Eternit* (2002). Photographic projects include *Symbolic Landscape* (*Pejzaż symboliczny*), an Upper Silesian coking plant under demolition; *An Anthology*, a book of portraits of authors; a record of religious events in Kalwaria Zebrzydowska; and *Black and White Silesia* (*Czarno-biały Śląsk*), on post-industrial areas. He is working on *Life after Life* (*Życie po życiu*), colour images of obsolete cars and *Post-Industrial*, black and white photographs documenting derelict industrial facilities.

Elżbieta Wójcik-Leese is a translator and editor. Her translations of Polish poetry appear regularly in UK and US periodicals. She co-edited *Carnivorous Boy Carnivorous Bird: Poetry from Poland* (Zephyr Press, USA, 2004). *Salt Monody*, poems by Marzanna Kielar, came out from Zephyr Press in 2006.